D1473387

EXCELLENCE ON THE HILL

A HISTORY OF
INTEGRIS BAPTIST
MEDICAL CENTER

Oklahoma Horizons Series

EXCELLENCE ON THE HILL
A HISTORY OF
INTEGRIS BAPTIST MEDICAL CENTER

By Bob Burke

Series Editor: Gini Moore Campbell
Associate Editor: Eric Dabney

OKLAHOMA HALL *of* FAME
OKLAHOMA HERITAGE ASSOCIATION PUBLISHING

2016 OFFICERS AND DIRECTORS

CHAIRMAN OF THE BOARD
Mark A. Stansberry, Edmond

CHAIRMAN-ELECT OF THE BOARD
Governor Bill Anoatubby, Ada

CHAIRMAN EMERITUS OF THE BOARD
Joe P. Moran III, Tulsa

VICE CHAIRMEN OF THE BOARD - EC
Phil B. Albert, Claremore
Bill Burgess, Jr., Lawton
Nevyle R. Cable, Okmulgee
Virginia G. Groendyke, Enid
Duke R. Ligon, Wewoka
Xavier Neira, Norman

CORPORATE SECRETARY
Amanda Clinton, Tulsa

TREASURER
Bruce T. Benbrook, Woodward

CHAIRMAN APPOINTMENTS
DIRECTORS AT LARGE - EC
Clayton I. Bennett, Oklahoma City
Glen D. Johnson, Oklahoma City
Vicki Miles-LaGrange, Oklahoma City

PRESIDENT & CEO
Shannon L. Rich, Oklahoma City

CHAIRMEN'S COUNCIL
Calvin J. Anthony, Stillwater
Pat Henry, Lawton
Roxana Lorton, Tulsa
Tom J. McDaniel, Oklahoma City
Lee Allan Smith, Oklahoma City
G. Lee Stidham, Checotah

DIRECTORS
Alison Anthony, Sand Springs
Bob Burke, Oklahoma City
Steve Burrage, Antlers
Ann L. Caine, Oklahoma City
Stan Clark, Stillwater
Mick Cornett, Oklahoma City
Teresa Rose Crook, Edmond
Chad Dillingham, Enid
Rebecca Dixon, Tulsa
Gentner F. Drummond, Tulsa
Greg Elliott, Chickasha
Ken Fergeson, Altus
Malinda Berry Fischer, Stillwater
Jennifer M. Grigsby, Oklahoma City
Joe D. Hall, Elk City
Fred Harlan, Okmulgee
Steve Hendrickson, Oklahoma City
Robert Henry, Oklahoma City
Rhonda Hooper, Oklahoma City
Gary Huckabay, Yukon
Ronnie Irani, Oklahoma City
Kirk Jewell, Stillwater

Rebecca Keesling, Tulsa
John Massey, Durant
John M. McArthur, Lawton
Frank W. Merrick, Oklahoma City
Bond Payne, Oklahoma City
Gregory E. Pyle, Durant
T. Hastings Siegfried, Tulsa
Michael E. Smith, Oklahoma City
C. Renzi Stone, Oklahoma City
Clayton C. Taylor, Oklahoma City
Kathy Taylor, Tulsa
Steven W. Taylor, McAlester
Stratton Taylor, Claremore
Steve Turnbo, Tulsa
Michael C. Turpen, Oklahoma City
Hardy Watkins, Oklahoma City
Susan Winchester, Oklahoma City

©2016 Oklahoma Heritage Association Publishing, a publication of the Oklahoma Hall of Fame

All rights reserved. No part of this book may be reproduced or utilized in any form or by any means, electronic or mechanical, including photocopying and recording, by any information storage and retrieval system, without permission of the publisher.

Unless otherwise noted, photos courtesy of the INTEGRIS Baptist Medical Center.

Printed in Canada

ISBN: 978-1-938923-27-2
Library of Congress Control Number: 2016932064

DESIGN: SKIP MCKINSTRY
COVER PHOTO/ILLUSTRATION: COURTESY SKIP MCKINSTRY

Courtesy Axiz Photography and Toby Nabors

Courtesy Axiz Photography and Toby Nabors

Courtesy Axiz Photography and Toby Nabors

INTRODUCTION

Ever since Benjamin Franklin founded this country's first hospital in Philadelphia, Pennsylvania, the tradition of American hospitals has been one of a commitment to a single ideal—service to community with ever increasing technological excellence.

This selfless ideal was seized upon by men and women of great religious faith of all denominations—Protestants, Catholics, and Jews—individually establishing hospitals to bring their communities closer to God as part of a healing ministry. Catholic nuns traveled across the plains in covered wagons to extend their beliefs through charitable work in hospitals and schools. Baptists, Lutherans, and Methodists all saw their commitment to a healing ministry as a way to combine their evangelistic fervor with service to the poor and sick.

In Oklahoma, as in much of the South, the Baptist church, represented by individual state conventions, was especially active in this ministry. The Baptist

General Convention of Oklahoma, led by Dr. T.B. Lackey, realized by 1950 the time had come for there to be a large Baptist hospital presence in the capital city of Oklahoma, Oklahoma City.

The Convention, assisted by leading Baptist laymen, other prominent business leaders, and physicians of many faiths, put together a philanthropic campaign unlike any other seen in the state to that time. The hundreds of well wishers who gathered on Easter Sunday in 1959 to celebrate the grand opening of Baptist Hospital could little have imagined the spectacular growth that would take place over the next 50-plus years on what was then, and still is, the highest geographic point in Oklahoma City.

From the very beginning, Baptist Hospital, later Baptist Medical Center, was on a very special journey. Located at the apex of two highways in the growth corridor of the city, the lay and physician leaders of the hospital embarked on a path to excellence through specialization that was unknown in Oklahoma.

This book is the story of more than five decades of a single-minded focus on the goal of providing world class care to Oklahomans. The board, medical staff, and management want to thank Bob Burke, Gini Moore Campbell, and Oklahoma Heritage Association Publishing, a publication of the Oklahoma Hall of Fame, for their efforts in bringing this story to life. In the end, it is a story of Oklahomans who would accept no less than excellence in medical care and technology. It is the story of men and women of faith who never lost sight of the goal of ensuring their community and state would have access to the best medical care and, in the end, it is a story of physicians, nurses, and technicians who made the commitment to the mission, "Excellence on the Hill."

Stanley F. Hupfeld

Former President and CEO of INTEGRIS Baptist Medical Center, INTEGRIS Health, and Chairman of the INTEGRIS Family of Foundations

INTEGRIS

NTEGRIS
Heart Hospital

ough
ar Institute

Thorpe
habilitation Hospital

Nazih Zuhdi
Transplant Institute

Paul Silverstein
Burn Center

James R. Daniel
Cerebrovascular
& Stroke Center

Courtesy Axiz Photography and Toby Nabors

ACKNOWLEDGMENTS

Many people helped make this book possible.
Whenever I needed information or photographs,
Stan Hupfeld made it happen. For years Judy
Hoisington and Sally Ritcheson Burks collected
historical memorabilia and photographs as part
of the Heritage Room project.

Thanks also to Marshall Snipes, Hardy Watkins,
Anna Stewart, Suzan Whaley, and Dr. Galen Robbins
for their contributions. As always, I am indebted
to series editor Gini Moore Campbell and associate
editor Eric Dabney for their guidance. Gini has
now edited more than 50 of my books in her role as
vice president of publications and education for the
Oklahoma Hall of Fame. Eric has served as my law
office manager for more than two decades.

I am grateful that Oklahoma Heritage Association
Publishing, a publication of the Oklahoma Hall of Fame
sees fit to publish histories such as this to preserve the
marvelous story of the people of Oklahoma.

Bob Burke—2015

Courtesy Axiz Photography and Toby Nabors

EXCELLENCE
ON THE HILL
A HISTORY OF
INTEGRIS BAPTIST
MEDICAL CENTER

Courtesy Axiz Photography and Toby Nabors

CHAPTER 1

A Dream Becomes Reality

Building a hospital
in Oklahoma's capital city had long been
a dream of Baptists in the state. Shortly after
the Baptist General Convention was formed
in 1906, Baptists in Muskogee began
planning for a hospital for their town to fulfill
the denominational belief that the presence
of a Baptist hospital in a community was
both an agent for healing the sick and
an evangelistic ministry to non-Christians.

Dr. T.B. Lackey, executive secretary-treasurer of the Baptist General Convention of Oklahoma, kept the dream of a Baptist hospital for Oklahoma City alive for nearly ten years before it became a reality. Legend has it that he often went to the hilltop where the hospital was eventually built and prayed for its success.

In 1909, the first Baptist hospital in Oklahoma opened at Muskogee. In 1918, Miami Baptist Hospital began accepting patients in northeast Oklahoma. By the 1940s, the Baptist General Convention operated hospitals in Muskogee, Mangum, Miami, and Enid. At the end of World War II, many smaller Oklahoma towns began building new hospitals. Within a short period of time, Baptists took over operation of community hospitals in Perry, Stillwater, Pryor, and Bristow.

Decades before, a Baptist hospital had existed in Oklahoma City for a short time. In 1918, the Baptist General Convention paid $29,000 for a privately-owned 24-bed hospital at Northwest 12th Street and Walker Avenue in Oklahoma City. The Convention operated the hospital until it became a huge financial burden in 1926. The hospital later became Oklahoma City General Hospital, and ultimately Mercy Hospital.

As Oklahoma City grew, and the need for additional hospital beds became well known, many leading Baptists again talked of building a Baptist hospital. At first, it was not a popular idea among some Baptist leaders. The older leaders remembered the financial drain of the previous hospital. Others were aware of the expansion of existing hospitals—St. Anthony, Wesley, Mercy, and University. Surely, they said, the last thing Oklahoma City needed was a new hospital. In addition, the Baptist General Convention did not own any property on which to build a facility and had no funds for such a project.

Baptists, at their statewide meeting on December 3, 1946, announced the appointment of a committee to actively plan for building a hospital in Oklahoma City. It was a star-studded committee headed by leading Baptist layman Robert S. Kerr. Raised as a conservative Southern Baptist in Pontotoc County, Kerr attended Oklahoma Baptist University, taught Sunday school, and was in the last month of his term as Governor of Oklahoma when appointed to the Baptist Hospital Committee. Other members of the committee were Dr. Andrew Potter, longtime executive secretary-treasurer of the Baptist General Convention of Oklahoma, R.C. Howard, Sr., president of the Baptist General Convention of Oklahoma, Willis R. Howard, and United States District Judge W.R. Wallace.

At the first meeting of the committee, members unanimously agreed that no less than one million dollars should be spent to build a Baptist hospital in Oklahoma City. They agreed to "pray about it" and think about launching a fund-raising campaign. R.C. Howard, Sr., was awakened at 3:30 a.m. one morning and wrote a letter titled, "Should Baptists Have a

Hospital in Oklahoma City?" He asked interested Baptists to contribute to the effort. He said, "Not a dollar will be used unless and until the hospital is established." Howard was convinced he was doing the right thing. He said, "If this plan is of the Lord, it will be accomplished."

Unfortunately, Howard did not live to see his dream realized. Within a short period of time, both he and Convention secretary-treasurer Potter died. Because of their deaths and other urgent matters related to change in leadership of the Convention, plans for a hospital were temporarily placed on the back burner.

Potter's assistant, Dr. T.B. Lackey, was elected to the top fulltime position of the Convention at its 1951 annual meeting. Because he had first-hand knowledge of the worthiness of the project, Lackey immediately began to challenge Baptists in Oklahoma to do more than just talk about building a denominational hospital in Oklahoma City. Still, Lackey's efforts faced an uphill climb. It was not a small task to build an institution from the ground up.

From the moment he stepped into leadership of Oklahoma Baptists, Lackey's deep conviction of the need for a Baptist hospital was unquestioned. In his first address to the Convention, Lackey made a strong plea for building a new hospital. His mission was clear:

> Not only is it our dream to have a large hospital caring for thousands of people, but it is our desire to have the best in medical and spiritual service. We are determined, with the Lord's help, to operate the hospital in the strongest possible spiritual atmosphere. We believe that medical science and the spiritual emphasis can work together in maximum treatment of body, soul, and mind.

To gain support for his renewed effort, Lackey approached perhaps the most influential Baptist preacher in the state, Dr. Herschel Hobbs, pastor of First Baptist Church of Oklahoma City. Dr. Hobbs made the motion to appoint a new committee to "look into the matter of locating a Baptist hospital in Oklahoma City and recommend a site."

The new committee included Kerr, who had been elected to the United States Senate, Judge Wallace, M.E. Ramay, Bryce Twitty, Auguie Henry, Anson Justice, Raymond A. Young, Dr. Lackey, and Dr. Hobbs as chairman. Young was one of the founders of the TG&Y retail store chain.

For the first time, a serious effort began to make the dream a reality. The St. Louis, Missouri, consulting firm of Bartholomew and Associates was hired

FOUNDING HOSPITAL COMMITTEE

Robert S. Kerr

Andrew Potter

R.C. Howard, Sr.

Willis R. Howard

W.R. Wallace

TG&Y Stores founder Raymond A. Young was a member of the Baptist Hospital Committee that brought about construction of the hospital.

5

Dr. Herschel Hobbs, back row, left, and Dr. T.B. Lackey look over documents reflecting the gift of Edith, Lottie, and Myrtle Shepherd of 10 acres at Northwest 30th Street and Villa Avenue for the construction of what would be known as the Shepherd Memorial Baptist Hospital.

to determine if another hospital in Oklahoma was needed. The survey's results were powerful—there was an immediate need for 455 additional beds and Oklahoma City would need 1,100 new hospital beds by 1960. The firm suggested building a 500-bed hospital, in stages, and provide for a school of nursing.

In June, 1953, with the feasibility study in hand, Baptist officials met with civic leaders who heartily endorsed the idea for more hospital beds in the Oklahoma City metropolitan area. The Oklahoma City Chamber of Commerce had adopted a slogan, "600,000 by 1960," which predicted unprecedented growth in Oklahoma, Cleveland, and Canadian counties in central Oklahoma as many rural Oklahomans moved to the cities. Frankly, the low number of beds in existing hospitals was a negative for potential new businesses that were concerned about the availability of quality health care for their workers.

A Texas fund-raising firm was chosen to develop a plan to raise $2.5 million, of which $1.5 million would come from Baptist churches in the state. Lieutenant General Raymond S. McLain was selected as chairman of the fund-raising effort. Hopes were high, but were quickly dashed when General McLain died. Civic leaders' support cooled. T.B. Lackey's biographer, Sam Scantlan, said, "Lackey's heart was heavy. It seemed for a time that our dreams were completely shattered and that there would be no Baptist hospital in Oklahoma City."

The hospital committee worked on, although slowly. There was no unanimity on a site for a hospital and fund-raising efforts were at a standstill. Some committee members wanted to reduce the size of the proposed 500-bed hospital to perhaps less than 200 beds. The result was a substantial reduction in the original construction cost estimate of $4 million.

The Baptist General Convention officially approved the hospital project. On June 28, 1954, the Oklahoma City Appeals Review Board authorized a public fund-raising plan to raise $500,000 to be matched by the Convention. The city government action cleared the way for picking up the hospital plans that were shelved the previous year. It was a reduced effort, but in the eyes of Baptist leaders, "it was the best that could be attained."

Dr. Hobbs' committee asked churches and the public to suggest a building site for the hospital. Three sisters, Edith, Lottie, and Myrtle Shepherd, owned the largest tract of undeveloped land within the city limits. The land, between Northwest 23rd and Northwest 30th streets between Villa and Pennsylvania avenues, later was the site of the Shepherd Mall shopping center. It was part of the original piece of land claimed by the sisters' father, George, in the Oklahoma Land Run of 1889. The Shepherd sisters offered to donate 10 acres at the corner of Northwest 30th Street and Villa Avenue for the construction of the hospital. The land was valued at approximately $500,000.

The benevolence of the Shepherd sisters seemed to jumpstart the Baptist hospital project. On March 12, 1955, 29 Oklahoma City civic leaders met in the home of oilman Frank Buttram. R.J. Spradling, president of the Oklahoma City Chamber of Commerce, presided over the meeting as interested citizens began talking about their dream. After Dr. Donald Branham, president of the Oklahoma County Medical Society, spoke of the critical need for hospital facilities, Virgil Browne, asked to be heard.

In a solemn voice, he said, "One thought strikes me this evening. Some of our loved ones, someone in this room, may die because we do not have these hospital facilities now."

Browne's comments duly noted the seriousness of the Planning Committee meeting. Committee chairman, Judge Wallace, presented a formal plan for the Shepherd Memorial Baptist Hospital. He noted that Oklahoma City's four largest hospitals were running near 90 percent occupancy and that Oklahoma ranked far below the national average in number of hospital beds per 1,000 population. The host, Buttram, talked about the challenge that pioneers in Oklahoma faced, and conquered, and urged his guests to "step up to ease mankind's suffering."

Senator Kerr, already on his way to becoming the "uncrowned king of the U.S. Senate," suggested that the building of the hospital was key to the development of Oklahoma City. He said, "If we don't want to be bedeviled, let's put up a sign that says, 'We don't want to grow anymore.' Then we would have no need for hospital beds."

Kerr stressed the importance of substantial gifts in a capital funds campaign. At the meeting, he was followed by E.K. Gaylord, a superb community leader and publisher of *The Daily Oklahoman.* Gaylord reminded the leaders of how two packing plants had been attracted to Oklahoma City by community

Governor Raymond Gary, left, was a Baptist deacon from Madill. He strongly supported the building of a Baptist hospital in Oklahoma City. In April, 1955, he announced the appointment of builder W.P. "Bill" Atkinson, center, as general chairman of the fund-raising drive. At right is Federal Judge W.R. Wallace, a member of the Hospital Committee of the Baptist General Convention of Oklahoma.

leaders' efforts. He said, "We should encourage giv-ing in the same terms that our pioneer families gave. Such gifts would be multiplied a thousand-fold."

The leaders unanimously agreed to immediately begin the fund-raising effort. Oklahoma Governor Raymond Gary, himself a staunch Baptist, wrote a confident letter of support:

> I cannot too strongly emphasize to the people of Oklahoma City the importance of increas-ing the number of hospital beds and improved facilities, or the many advantages that such action will bring.

Senator Kerr articulated the lateness of the hour for building a Baptist hospital:

> This campaign could not have been post-poned one more day without affecting may lives in our community. We welcome the opportunity to participate in building a hos-pital and realize the sound reasons that are behind the action.

Kerr suggested that W.P. "Bill" Atkinson, the land developer who built the Oklahoma City suburb of Midwest City, be named chairman of the fund-rais-ing campaign organization. Governor Gary was honorary chairman and Judge Wallace was chair-man of the Planning Committee.

The Planning Committee for the 1955 campaign met in the home of oilman Frank Buttram. Among the group were, left to right, R.J. Spradling, Oklahoma City Federal Savings and Loan; advertising executive Lowe Runkle; Stanley Draper of the Oklahoma City Chamber of Commerce; architect Truett Coston; and attorney Joe Rucks.

Key to the success of planning a capital campaign to build Baptist Memorial Hospital were, left to right, Judge W.R. Wallace, Virgil Browne, Senator Robert S. Kerr, and E.K. Gaylord.

The official campaign letterhead listed 36 prominent men representing all segments of the community. Among the members were business and civic leaders Fred Jones, Donald S. Kennedy, Virgil Browne, B.D. Eddie, Harvey P. Everest, E.K. Gaylord, Stanley Draper, and S.N. Goldman, the inventor of the shopping cart.

To advise the capital campaign, Dr. Henry G. Bennett, Jr., was chairman of a Physicians Advisory Committee composed of Drs. Donald W. Branham, J. Hartwell Dunn, Eugene F. Lester, Milton J. Serwer, and Ralph A. Smith. Reverend Grady C. Cothen was named chairman of a Church Advisory Committee, and advertising executive Lowe Runkle served as chairman of the Public Information Committee.

The fund-raising campaign officially began on April 5, 1955. Supporters were shown drawings of a multi-story hospital produced by the architectural firm of Coston, Frankfurt & Short. That firm, fresh from designing additions to University Hospital, was chosen from a field of eight firms submitting proposals.

At the kickoff dinner, Bryce Twitty, administrator of Hillcrest Hospital in Tulsa, said "Sick people cannot pay for care and for brick and mortar too," emphasizing that the healthy citizens of the community needed to step forward and fund construction of the hospital. E.K. Gaylord spoke to the group. His theme was, "All big things done is this town have been done by voluntary groups."

By May 16, contributions to the campaign topped $500,000. Senator Kerr donated $75,000; Oklahoma Natural Gas Company, $50,000; TG&Y Stores, E.K. Gaylord, and Bill Atkinson, $25,000 each; V.V. Harris, R.C. Howard, and the Women's Missionary Union, $15,000 each; and B.D. Eddie and an anonymous donor, $10,000 each.

On June 3, committee members appeared at the Friday Forum of the Oklahoma City Chamber of Commerce to report that the fund-raising drive was only $70,000 short of its $1 million goal. Special recognition was given to Stanley Draper, executive director of the Oklahoma City Chamber of Commerce, for his leadership in the effort.

The architects were told to complete plans and contracts were let for site preparation at Northwest 30th and Villa. However, there was a problem. A subcommittee of the Oklahoma City Planning and Zoning Commission was rumored to be considering rejecting the application to open new streets and widen existing streets around the site. There was concern that the ten-acre plot of land donated by the Shepherd sisters was not sufficient for suitable parking, a doctor's office building, nursing school, and future expansion.

On June 9, the Planning and Zoning Commission, calling the plan to build the hospital on such a small

By July 23, 1956 work had begun on preparing the site for the new Baptist hospital "out in the country" in northwest Oklahoma City.

tract of land "a monster of mis-planning," refused to rezone the property. Hospital leaders were forced to decline the generous offer of the Shepherd sisters, but Dr. Lackey said, "We will build the hospital."

Quickly, he and campaign leaders looked for a larger tract of land. A Site Selection Sub-Committee was appointed. Its members included civic leaders Bill Atkinson, E.K. Gaylord, and B.D. Eddie; physicians Henry G. Bennett, Jr., Elmer Ridgeway, Jr., and J. Hartwell Dunn; and Dr. Hobbs, Judge Wallace, and Dr. M.E. Ramay, representing the Baptist General Convention of Oklahoma.

Over the next few months, the committee considered 12 different locations. One option was to purchase five blocks on Northeast 13th Street east of University Hospital. Other possible sites were 27 acres at Northeast 25th Street and Lottie Avenue, a 60-acre tract at Northwest 39th Street and Portland Avenue, and a parcel of land near Northwest 50th Street and Pennsylvania Avenue. Donations of land from Ella Classen, Ben Wileman, and Walter Jones were refused because the tracts were too small.

Inundated by offers, the Site Selection Subcommittee named Atkinson, Bennett, and Wallace as a steering group to set criteria for selection of a construction site. They determined that four needs had to be met—accessibility, good topography, a decent view, and a population growth area.

After substantial time was spent looking at several parcels of property, the Site Selection Subcommittee settled on a 22-acre tract of land on Northwest Highway. The property was bounded on the north by the four-lane highway and on the west by Grand Boulevard. It was only a short distance from May Avenue and US-66. The elevation at 1,282 feet above sea level was 86 feet higher than downtown Oklahoma City. The view was excellent—Lake Hefner and much of the northwest side of the city could be seen. The fourth criterion of the selection committee also was met—population experts predicted that the center of growth in Oklahoma City for the next 25 years would be near the proposed hospital location.

The Hospital Committee of the Baptist General Convention, chaired by Dr. Hobbs, approved the site and authorized the signing of a contract for purchase of the land on December 6, 1955. The $145,000 cost of the property was reduced by a $55,000 gift from Leroy Smith and James B. Battle, Jr. The remaining portion of the purchase price of $90,000 was underwritten by the West Side Chamber of Commerce. The Baptist General Convention purchased an adjoining 40 acres for $175,000. Dr. Hobbs was thrilled that the entire 62-acre tract was purchased for a fraction of the price that the owners of another site wanted.

Even though Baptist leaders were happy with the choice of the property, there were many doubters in the community. Civic and church leaders were met with comments that the property was "so far away from downtown." Some predicted the hospital would go broke if it was built so far "out in the country." A front-page headline in The Daily Oklahoman said, "Site for $15-Million Hospital Center Selected by Baptists."

Dr. Lackey, confident that Baptists had chosen the perfect spot for a hospital, said, "The selection of this land ensures a medical center comparable to any in the southwest." It had been nine years since the first public suggestion that a Baptist hospital be built in Oklahoma City. As Lackey and others walked among the prairie dog holes and rocks on the vacant land on the hill, they surely could not adequately envision the emergence of excellence that would occur during the next decades.

The first architect's drawing of the proposed Baptist Memorial Hospital. The rendering was created by the architectural firm of Coston, Frankfurt & Short.

Courtesy Axiz Photography and Toby Nabors

CHAPTER 2

Selecting the Right People

A site had been selected
and there was money in the bank to finance
most of the hospital's construction.
The next order of business was to pick an
administrator and medical director. The
Baptist Laymen's Corporation held title to the
land and its board met to choose leadership.
Dr. Lackey thought the administrator should
be a Baptist preacher. Others, including
Dr. J. Hartwell Dunn and Raymond A. Young,
believed the administrator should be trained
in hospital administration. Young said,
"This hospital is going to be a business
proposition from start to finish, and it needs
a businessman to handle things."

John M. Hendricks was the first administrator of Baptist Memorial Hospital.

Dr. J. Hartwell Dunn was one of the doctors who urged the building of Baptist Memorial Hospital. He was a department head when the hospital opened.

Dr. Dunn agreed with Young and told Lackey, "You can't have a preacher who is not in medicine running a hospital. It's too late in history for that." After a series of candidate interviews, John Hendricks was hired as Baptist Memorial Hospital's first administrator on February 20, 1956. Hendricks was 37 years old, a native of Tennessee, a pharmacist, and held a masters degree in hospital administration from the University of Minnesota. At the time he was hired, Hendricks was assistant administrator at the 900-bed Baptist Memorial Hospital in Memphis, Tennessee.

Lackey and Hendricks worked with the Baptist General Convention's Building Committee to finalize plans for construction. A groundbreaking ceremony was set for May 17, 1956. Nearly 4,000 people attended a free barbecue dinner at which the Northwest Classen High School band entertained guests and Oklahoma City Mayor Allen Street extended greetings on behalf of the city. Speakers included Bill Atkinson, Dr. Max Stanfield, president of the Baptist General Convention of Oklahoma, and Dr. Lackey, who announced that the $2 million in contributions and appropriation from the Convention would not be enough to complete the hospital. He said another $1 million would be needed.

By November, 1956, plans were still not complete. Even though groundbreaking had occurred months before, changes in the plans delayed awarding of construction contracts. The architects worked with administrator Hendricks and Dr. Lackey to finalize details of the building which was described as the first unit of a layout that would include a Golden Age Home for retired persons, a nursing school, a home, and a church. A parking lot that could accommodate several hundred cars was an integral part of the plan. Baptist churches in Oklahoma set aside May 5, 1957, as "Dedicated Dollar Day," the taking of a special offering to be applied to construction costs.

On February 22, 1957, a $3.3 million contract was awarded to the G.E. Bass Company. In May, a newly-organized Baptist Memorial Hospital (BMH) advisory board was created. Judge Wallace was chairman, General William S. Key was named vice chairman, and Hugh Harrell was selected as secretary. Other advisory board members included Governor Raymond Gary, Carl B. Anderson, A.J. Haswell, H. Cecil Webb, Bill Atkinson, Faye E. Hixson, Jean I. Everest, O.C. Brown, Neal B. Pritchard, R.C. Howard, Reverend Murray Fuquay, and Reverend Tom Carter. It was also announced that financial arrangements had been made to complete construction.

In July, the building permit was issued by the City of Oklahoma City. The specific plan approved was for 200 beds on seven floors with 156,796 square feet of floor space. It was estimated that equipment for the hospital would cost $800,000. With the permit issued and plans completed, massive dirt work began to redefine the hillside upon which the hospital would be placed.

With construction underway, Dr. Henry G. Bennett, Jr., began to recruit physicians to form a medical staff. Many Oklahoma City doctors watched the new building rise from the ground and committed themselves to seek privileges to practice there. Dr. Robert Anspaugh was one of the first physicians to enthusiastically join the new team, promising Bennett that he would head up the OB-GYN department when the hospital opened. Both Bennett and Anspaugh were part of a national movement to better organize medical staffs at hospitals.

One of the new staff members was James L. "Jay" Henry, a 29-year-old Midwest City native who graduated from Oklahoma Baptist University and earned a masters degree in hospital administration from Northwestern University. Henry was hired as Hendricks' administrative assistant. Henry had served in the Army's medical service, worked at a hospital in Amarillo, Texas, and most recently was the administrator of Parkview Hospital in El Reno, Oklahoma.

Henry arrived on the job just in time for the laying of the cornerstone of the hospital on November 13, 1958. Dr. Lackey, Judge Wallace, and Stanley Draper made presentations before Hendricks actually laid the cornerstone and Tom Carter, who oversaw hospital operations for the Baptist General Convention of Oklahoma, unveiled the cornerstone plaque. The official program for the occasion listed 250 individuals, 85 businesses, and 95 Baptist churches throughout the state that had each contributed more than $500 to the building project.

It was a red-letter day for Baptists and all Oklahomans on Easter Sunday, March 19, 1959, when residents of the capital city were invited to come see the new Baptist Memorial Hospital with a price tag that had escalated to $4.6 million. Behind the scenes, leaders made arrangements to borrow money to be able to move into the hospital.

Ten thousand people accepted the invitation that was included in a special section of *The Sunday Oklahoman*. It was a popular event because it was the first time since 1930 that a new hospital had opened in the capital city. Automobiles were parked on streets a half mile in every direction. The seven-story Y-shaped building, an attached service building, and a connecting tunnel were defined in red brick, black granite, and cream-colored precast

Dr. Henry G. Bennett, Jr., was an active supporter of the effort to build Baptist Memorial Hospital and was the hospital's first chief of staff. Assistant Administrator, and later longtime Administrator Jay Henry said, "The primary reason that Baptist Medical Center became great was the early work of Dr. Bennett in organizing the medical staff and creating a strict set of standards by which physicians were given privileges to practice at the new hospital." Dr. Bennett was highly trained at Johns Hopkins and had a unique vision of organizing the medical staff with officers, an executive committee, and a clinical component.

concrete. Visitors crowded hallways to inspect and admire six floors of patient rooms, nursing stations, waiting rooms, laboratory areas, and surgical suites. The power plant, officials said, was large enough to serve a town the size of Yukon.

The new hospital was pleasing to the eye. Historian Gloria Howe Bremkamp wrote:

> The place was pretty, too. Pastels predominated. Corridors and work areas blossomed in pink, beige, yellow, and blue ceramic tile. Casework throughout was pink, contrasting handsomely with doors, furnishings, and telephone booths of walnut Formica. Acoustically treated ceilings overriding floors of vinyl, quarry tile, and terrazzo restrained noise levels.

The hospital opened for business on April 9 with 206 employees. "It was chaos," remembered Dr. E. Neal Holden. The first patient, W.I. Hagar, was admitted on April 14. Five days later, on April 19, the first baby was born. Laurie Lynn Gibson, daughter of Shirley Gibson, was delivered by Dr. Robert Anspaugh in a tuxedo. The doctor had been at a dance with his wife when notified that Mrs. Gibson

The original cornerstone of the hospital was laid on November 13, 1958.

A newspaper said the new Baptist Memorial Hospital was "a push button marvel, with electronic gadgets taking over a sizeable share of the work load, making employees' work easier, and adding to the patients' comfort."

An informative brochure given to guests at the hospital open house on Easter Sunday, 1959, touted the facility's "modern" qualities:

A symphony in stainless steel, the facilities at Baptist Memorial Hospital provide the ultimate in comfort and convenience for patient and worker alike. Nothing has been spared to ensure the finest service and most complete care for all who enter. Sterilizing equipment is just one example.

Oxygen outlets in every patient room eliminate the need for bulky tanks in the corridors.

Oxygen may be quickly and safely administered to patients without inconvenience or dangerous delays.

From his bed the patient is in constant contact with the nurse at her station by an ultra-modern call system. He may listen to his favorite radio program or to soothing music with complete control over the volume—without disturbing his fellow patients.

The new hospital opened with the latest in available technology in the surgical unit.

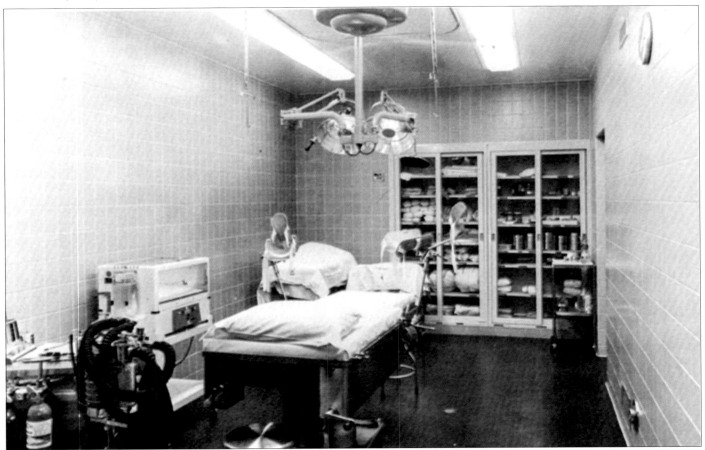

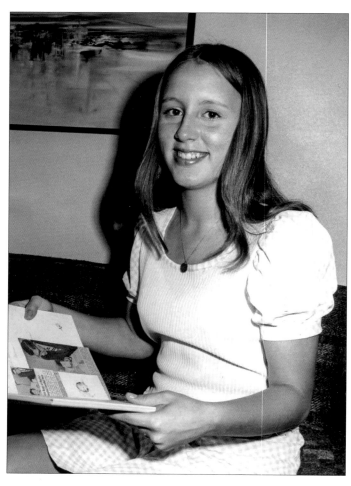

Laurie Lynn Gibson, the first baby born at Baptist Memorial Hospital, on her 15th birthday.

Dr. Thomas P. Haskins was the first chaplain of Baptist Memorial Hospital.

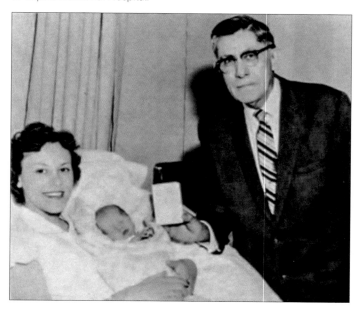

was in labor. He arrived at the hospital with no time to change into a scrub suit. Instead, he took off his jacket and put the surgical gown over the rest of his tuxedo. He later said, "It was certainly the most formal delivery I ever made!"

Day-to-day management of the new hospital was the responsibility of a governing board that in turn was responsible to the board of directors of the Baptist General Convention. Members of the first Governing Board were R.H. Nicholson, chairman; H.B. Lee, vice chairman; Mrs. George Miller, Jr., secretary; Reverend Tom Carter; Reverend Murray Fuquay; Gene Warr, Mrs. Ollie B. Stone, Dr. Max Stanfield, and R.C. Howard.

In March, the hospital received accreditation from the Joint Commission on the Accreditation of Hospitals. Dr. Bennett, appointed by the Governing Board as Chief of Staff, headed a provisional committee for staff organization that included many of the doctors who moved their primary place of practice to Baptist. The committee included Drs. Anspaugh, John F. Burton, Richard E. Carpenter, H.D. Dodson, Jr., J. Hartwell Dunn, Charles L. Freede, Allen E. Greer, Lynn H. Harrison, James R. Reed, Elmer Ridgeway, Jr., Frank W. Stewart, O. Alton Watson, W.K. West, and Harry Wilkins.

The staffing committee tackled the problem of having doctors perform treatment protocols for which they were trained. Dr. Bennett proposed that only board-certified or board-eligible physicians be allowed to practice their specialty at BMH. Jay Henry said, "He simply wanted the best available doctors to practice at the hospital." All other Oklahoma City hospitals permitted non board-certified practitioners to see patients in their institutions. Judy Hoisington, who later handled credentialing for doctors at the hospital, said, "It was an important step for the hospital when Dr. Bennett convinced the board of directors that only the most highly-trained doctors be given privileges at the new hospital."

Money problems plagued the new hospital. Even though the building was designed for 188 beds, only one unit was operating and two floors were open. More workers were needed, but there was no money in the budget. When Hendricks had to borrow another $300,000, Lackey and the Baptist General Convention board took severe action. Lackey appeared in Jay Henry's office in March, 1960, and announced that Hendricks was leaving and that he, Henry, would be acting administrator. Lackey told Henry to move into Hendricks' office before the end of the day. Hendricks had operated the hospital only for its first 11 months of existence.

A new parking lot is added to the north side of the new hospital in 1960. Note the hospital's neighboring buildings along the Northwest Highway. Above the Texaco station is the screen of the Northwest Highway Drive-In Theater, a popular destination for families of the era.

HOSPITAL'S FIRST GOVERNING BOARD

R.H. Nicholson, chairman
Mrs. George Miller, Jr.
Reverend Tom Carter
Reverend Murray Fuquay
Gene Warr
Mrs. Ollie B. Stone
Dr. Max Stanfield
R.C. Howard

FIRST MEDICAL STAFF AND DEPARTMENT HEADS

Dr. Henry G. Bennett, Jr.
Chief of Staff

Dr. R. Gibson Parrish
Anesthesiology

Dr. Frank W. Stewart
Dentistry and Oral Surgery

Dr. John M. Brown
General Practice

Dr. E.E. Cooke
General Surgery

Dr. William R. Paschal
Internal Medicine

Dr. Harry Wilkins
Neurosurgery

Dr. Robert D. Anspaugh
Obstetrics-Gynecology

Dr. James R. Reed
Ophthalmology

Dr. W.K. West
Orthopedic Surgery

Dr. Jack Van Doren Hough
Otolaryngology

Dr. DeWitt T. Hunter
Pathology

Dr. Charles L. Freede
Pediatrics

Dr. Hubert M. Anderson
Plastic Surgery

Dr. Wayne Schultz
Radiology

Dr. J. Hartwell Dunn
Urology

Dr. Charles Freede was the first head of the Pediatrics Department at Baptist Memorial Hospital.

Jay Henry became administrator of Baptist Memorial Hospital on January 1, 1961.

An aerial view of the Baptist Memorial Hospital campus in 1963 following the completion of the Doctor's Medical Building south of the main hospital.

Inset: In August, 1960, the Governing Board approved construction of the Doctors' Medical Building south of the hospital. A groundbreaking ceremony for the structure was held on August 28. This is the architect's conception of the building, now called Building A.

BAPTIST "FIRSTS" IN THE 1960S

1960
- Baptist is first hospital in nation to receive full accreditation by the Joint Commission on Accreditation of Hospitals less than a year after opening
- Women's Auxiliary is organized

1962
- School of Nursing opens
- Children's World opens as first employer-sponsored, on-site daycare in Oklahoma City

1963
- First open heart surgery performed by Dr. Nazih Zuhdi

1964
- Intensive Care Unit created

1966
- Psychiatric Unit opens

One of the first two resident interns at Baptist Memorial Hospital was Dr. James Walraven. The other was Dr. Lyle Cartwright. The hospital was approved for internships in 1962 by the American Medical Association in record time, thanks to the effort of Dr. W.K. West. The first intern program director was Dr. Robert C. Brown.

Lackey had confidence in Henry and allowed him to begin the long process of placing the hospital on a sound financial foundation, promoting harmony among departments, and planning for future expansions. Tom Carter remembered, "With an awareness of the scope and problems pertaining to the financial responsibility of good administration, he continuously improved the financial structure of operation." Carter believed Henry was "the man for the job" because of his good public relations skills to create a team spirit that would "reach the medical staff, the patients, and the public."

On the first anniversary of the hospital, the statistical report showed 5,674 patients admitted, 773 births, and an average daily occupancy of 67 percent. On March 1, 1960, the first student began training in the Baptist Memorial Hospital School of Medical Technology. Baby number 1,000 was born on June 2, 1960, 14 months after the hospital opened. On June 26, 1960, Ora Mashburn was elected the first president of the Women's Auxiliary called the "Cheery, Cheery Reds." The purpose of the group was to strengthen the hospital's relationship with the community and hold down costs by performing many functions with the help of volunteers.

Jay Henry was officially appointed administrator of the hospital on January 1, 1961. A School of X-Ray Technology was launched. The Women's Auxiliary began its volunteer program in May, 1961, under the leadership of Helen Masheter. There was an emphasis on giving teenagers—the girls were called "candy stripers"—an opportunity to spend a few hours per week in service to the hospital.

As promised in the original concept for Baptist Memorial Hospital, a contract for construction of the School of Nursing Building was awarded to the Milner Construction Company in October, 1961. Part of the money for construction came from the Woman's Missionary Union of the Baptist General Convention. The following month, a dual ceremony was held to dedicate the new Doctors' Medical Building and to break ground for the School of Nursing Building.

The Baptist Memorial Hospital School of Nursing became a reality in 1962 when the three-year diploma program was moved from Oklahoma Baptist Hospital in Muskogee to Oklahoma City. Students' first year was spent at Oklahoma Baptist University where they took basic classes that would be a foundation of their nursing education.

In September, 1962, the School of Nursing Building was dedicated with the principal address by Dr. James R. Scales, president of Oklahoma Baptist University. The building included living quarters

The architect's drawing of the School of Nursing facilities east of the Doctor's Medical Building.

In 1962, Baptist Memorial Hospital began publication of a monthly newsletter called "Memo Random." The publication contained feature stories and photographs of current events. The July, 1963 edition featured the Central Service Department that provided everything from distilled water to syringes to other departments of the hospital.

The first Baptist Memorial Hospital School of Nursing graduating class in May, 1963. Front row, left to right, Betty Ruth Grubbs, Kay Hiatt, Jenette Gooch, and Sue Miesner. Back row, Ruth Hickey, Betty Jean Cook, Charlene Snyder, Linda Steele, and Carolyn Wilkinson. Graduate Jaquita Williams was not available for the photograph.

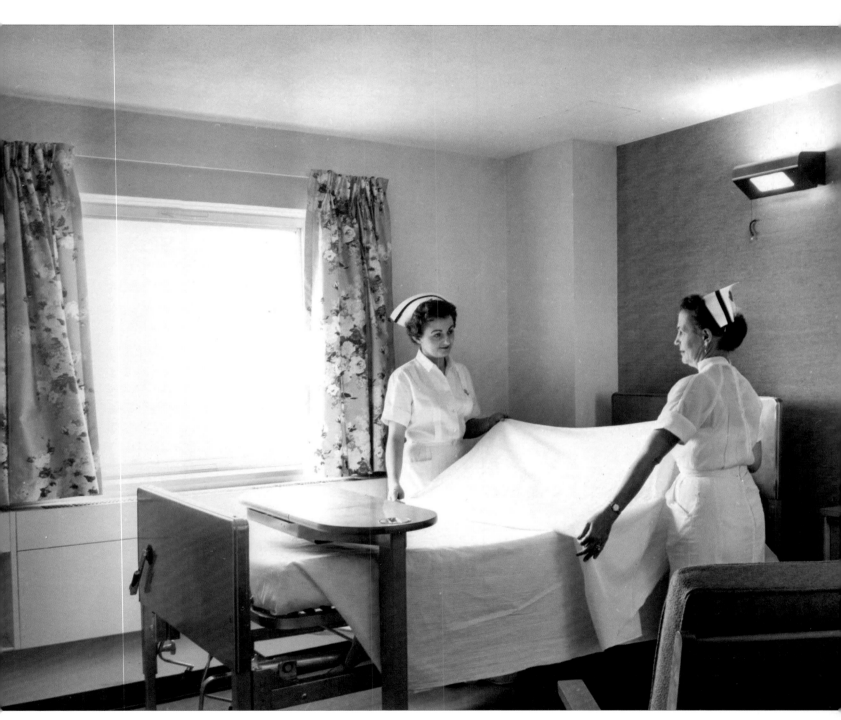

A modern patient's room in the new hospital in 1959.

The Volunteer Auxiliary became an integral part of the operation of Baptist Memorial Hospital soon after the hospital opened.

for 56 nursing students, a lounge, recreational space, a library, three classrooms, and offices for faculty members. The cost of the new structure was $335,000.

Nursing students spent their time on rotations at the hospital with physicians in various disciplines of treatment. They also were assigned to outside agencies such as the Dale Rogers Center. The nursing uniform was always white and had three quarters or full length sleeves. The nursing pin was awarded after the second year of study at the "capping" ceremony. The RN pin, usually attached with a tiny gold chain, was reserved for nurses who had earned the title by successfully completing their exams after the third year of study.

Six classes graduated from the BMH School of Nursing before the school moved to Central State College, now the University of Central Oklahoma, where it became a baccalaureate program. Elizabeth Weibe served as the Director of Nursing Education. When the nursing school closed on the BMH campus, the dormitory became the Administrative Services Building. Later the buildings were torn down to make way for the 56th Street Parking Garage.

Margaret Tucker was the first PBX operator at the hospital. The system allowed private telephone lines into each patient room.

Courtesy Axiz Photography and Toby Nabors

CHAPTER 3

Healthy Expansion and A Defining Moment

Even though the hospital had been open for only three years, there was substantial interest in expansion. Jay Henry said, "We already had a need for four additional patient care floors. Our good occupancy rate gave the perception to doctors that we could not handle any more patients. Pressure for more beds increased." Dr. J. Hartwell Dunn was a leading vocal proponent for expanding the hospital. He said physicians needed to be assured that sufficient beds would always be available to accommodate their patients.

1963 EXPANSION BUILDING COMMITTEE

Raymond A. Young, Chairman
James Battle
Reverend Frank Baugh
O.C. Brown
Reverend Harvey Elledge

Jay Henry, left, and Edward L. Gaylord participate in groundbreaking ceremonies for the West Tower in November, 1963.

R.C. Howard
H.B. Lee
Marvin Staton
Reverend Warren Terry
Dr. T.B. Lackey
Reverend William G. Kersh

In September, 1962, eight prominent Oklahoma City civic leaders met at Senator Robert S. Kerr's ranch near Poteau, Oklahoma, to talk about new medical facilities. Kerr used his well-known power of persuasion to express the need for substantial funds to construct a large expansion. Visiting one on one with his guests, Kerr was able to secure promises for $850,000 that weekend.

The new capital campaign's public goal was $1.5 million. Edward L. Gaylord of the Oklahoma Publishing Company was named general chairman. Assisting him was a group of Oklahoma City's finest and most respected leaders—Dean A. McGee of Kerr-McGee Corporation, James J. Doherty, Jr., of Western Electric, Harvey P. Everest of Liberty National Bank, Donald S. Kennedy of Oklahoma Gas and Electric Company, and Raymond A. Young of TG&Y Stores.

Other members of the fund-raising committee included Stanley Draper of the Oklahoma City Chamber of Commerce, Dr. Henry Bennett, Jr., Dr. J.R. Stacy, president of the Oklahoma County Medical Society, W.R. Wolfe of Oklahoma Gas and Electric Company, Marvin Staton of Springlake Park, James Battle, investment counselor, V.P. Crowe, a prominent lawyer, and Dr. Dean Robertson, president of the Oklahoma County Dental Society.

"Stanley Draper was the key to the fund-raising effort," Jay Henry remembered. "He spent count-less hours coordinating Chamber of Commerce members in calling on the city's business leaders to contribute to the project."

Plans were finalized to kickoff solicitations for funds in late January, 1963. However, on New Year's Day, Senator Kerr died, thwarting attempts to secure federal funding for part of the cost of expansion. But, with more than $2 million in pledges and a $500,000 donation from the Baptist General Convention of Oklahoma, money to build the West Tower was certain. Groundbreaking occurred on November 12, 1963, and a construction contract for $2.4 million was awarded to the J.J. Bollinger Construction Company.

Money raised in the successful fund-raising venture made possible the construction of four additional floors, allowing the bed-capacity of BMH to nearly double to 376. The building committee; the architectural firm of Coston, Frankfurt & Short; hospital consultants, Boone Powell and Associates of Dallas, Texas; hospital administrators; and physicians met numerous times to design the best possible facilities within the expanded structure.

The hospital's first intensive care unit, outpatient clinics, and occupational therapy facilities opened

The expansion project concluded in 1965 added four floors to the main hospital building.

Jimmy Ruth Henson holds her daughter, Chimene, one of the first babies born at the new Baptist Memorial Hospital.

Early physicians practicing at Baptist Memorial Hospital included, left to right, Dr. Charles Monnet, Dr. William O. Coleman, Dr. William E. Hood, Jr., and Dr. Bobby Gene Smith.

Donald S. Kennedy, longtime president of Oklahoma Gas and Electric Company, was a member of the Governing Board and an ardent supporter of expanding the services of Baptist Memorial Hospital.

Oilman William T. Payne was a member of the Governing Board in 1969.

and the clinical laboratory, physical therapy unit, and surgical and obstetric departments were expanded. In addition, six stories were added to the Doctor's Medical Building, greatly increasing office space for physicians whose primary practice was at the hospital.

Drs. Galen Robbins and John J. Donnell established the hospital's first Radioisotope Laboratory and implemented plans for cardiac catheterization. Baptist, for two years, had been slowly, but definitively, moving toward excellence in the treatment of heart disease which had become a leading cause of death in the United States.

In 1963, Dr. Nazih Zuhdi performed the first open heart surgery at BMC. Dr. Zuhdi, recognized as one of the original pioneers of the modern treatment of heart disease, three years before had developed the Total Intentional Hemodilution process that revolutionized successful open-heart surgery procedures worldwide and paved the way for future heart transplants. That 1963 surgery was a defining moment in the history of BMC.

The first open heart surgery was anything but a lavish production. It began on April 1, 1963, when a borrowed pickup truck delivered Zuhdi's heart-lung machine and auxiliary equipment to BMC. Dr. Zuhdi oversaw the removal of the equipment to the surgery floor and an operating room. Assisted in surgery by Dr. John Carey, the patient did so well he was sent home two weeks later. Dr. Zuhdi's biographer, Brooks Barr, wrote, "Zuhdi was inaugurating his dream to expand open heart surgery in the entire world."

During the next two years, Dr. Zuhdi and his colleagues many times repeated the move of equipment from their laboratory at Mercy Hospital to BMC to perform open-heart surgeries there. Finally, "tired of lugging the machine up and down," Dr. Zuhdi left his heart-lung machine in the corner of a hallway in the BMC operating suite, and threw a sheet over it to discourage curious onlookers.

In 1964, a new 23-bed psychiatric unit was among new services of the hospital. The latest and most modern furnishings and equipment were featured in the four new floors of the hospital. Electric retractable beds, which cost $500 each, a lavatory, and private bath were included in the new adult patient rooms. By the time the new construction was completed in 1965, more than 50,000 patients had been admitted and 9,000 babies born in the hospital.

As Administrator Henry added personnel to facilitate the use of new space, the new Medicare law took effect. Henry used a new in-house publication, *The Quarterly Review,* to inform his staff and physicians about the sweeping provisions of the new law that would affect medical services to older and disabled Oklahomans. It was anticipated that with the advent of Medicare, demand for medical care would dramatically increase and hasten the need for further expansion of BMH.

Henry said, "Medicare gave us an increase in patient load we had scarcely imagined. By the end of the 1960s, we were putting patients in the hallways and in any alcove we could find."

Between 1967 and 1969, a special procedures room for heart catheterizations, a social service department, a planning and systems development department, a full-time medical librarian, and newborn intensive care unit were added. Dr. F.H. McGregor was named as Director of Medical Education, charged with coordinating continuing education programs for the medical staff.

With the increase in patient load, the Governing Board looked to the future. In 1969, board chairman R.C. Howard, Jr., said:

> We do not intend ever to be complacent. Although we believe we are now serving our patients and the community well, we are determined to seek constantly ways to improve and progress to meet health care needs of the future.

For the first time, hospital leaders implemented strategic planning efforts. Chief of Staff Dr. Bennett, Administrator Henry, and the Governing Board spent an intense six months defining the hospital's future. A special long-range planning committee was chaired by Raymond Young.

Members of the 1969 Governing Board who spent hundreds of hours in meetings with physicians and hospital management in strategic planning sessions were W. Kenneth Bonds, James Bullard, Reverend Ralph Crawford, Reverend J.P. Dane, Ferdie Deering, Donald Greve, R.C. Howard, James Johnson, Donald S. Kennedy, H.B. Lee, Helen Masheter, William T. Payne, Charles Truhitte, and Raymond A. Young. Baptist General Convention Executive Secretary Dr. T.B. Lackey was an ex-officio member.

Administrator Jay Henry was the key to the continued success of the hospital. Judy Hoisington joined his immediate staff as a receptionist in August, 1966, and soon became Henry's secretary, replacing her sister, Ann Schaff. Hoisington remembered, "He was a master of balancing the interests of all parties." The Baptist General Convention had to approve all members of the Governing Board. On several occasions, members' viewpoints on medical care widely differed with physicians practicing at the hospital. Hoisington said, "Jay had to answer to a lot

The first woman member of the Governing Board of Baptist Memorial Hospital was Helen Masheter, who also founded the Volunteer Auxiliary at the hospital.

Dr. Joe L. Ingram became executive director-treasurer of the Baptist General Convention of Oklahoma in 1971 and was a strong supporter of expansion of the medical center's expansion.

A $1 million fund-raising program was launched in early 1972 to finance Phase III construction. Left to right, Chief of Staff Dr. Henry G. Bennett, Jr., Nurse Dolores Lemon, chairman of the employee gift division, Virgie Barrett, president of the Volunteer Auxiliary, and C.A. "Pat" Henderson, chairman of the Gifts Committee.

A crane places a steel beam into place as the North Tower begins to take shape in August, 1972.

Dr. Lowell Milburn, the Baptist General Convention's director of child care, left, and Pat Wright, director of Children's World, at the opening of the dedication of new facilities in 1972. Children's World was the first, on-site corporate sponsored daycare in Oklahoma City. The first director was Kathryn Cashon, wife of hospital controller, Sturgis Cashon.

With the completion of Phase III construction in 1974, a new sign announced the name change of the hospital to Baptist Medical Center.

An aerial view reflects the significant change to the Baptist Medical Center skyline after the Phase III construction was completed.

BAPTIST "FIRSTS" IN THE 1970S

1970
- First Carpentier valve replacement in both the aortic and atrioventricular positions in North America by Dr. Nazih Zuhdi

1972
- Name of hospital is changed to Baptist Medical Center

1973
- First stabilized glutaraldehyde porcine aortic valve, manufactured by scientist Warren Hancock, used in both the aortic and atrioventricular positions in the world by Dr. Nazih Zuhdi

1975
- Burn Center opens

1976
- Cardiac Rehabilitation Unit opens

1978
- Cochlear Implant Clinic opens
- PACER Fitness Center established as nation's first hospital-based fitness program

1979
- Oklahoma's first adult cochlear implant performed by Dr. Jack Van Doren Hough

of people but always knew when to talk to certain people to advance an issue. Sometimes, he talked with a small group of board members before introducing an idea to the full board."

Henry had a unique relationship with doctors, especially with Dr. Bennett, the Chief of Staff. "Jay always did his homework," Hoisington reflected. "If doctors saw an issue one way, and the Governing Board saw it another way, Jay found common ground among the parties and prevented major disputes from erupting."

The hospital celebrated its tenth anniversary in April, 1969. The occasion was marked with a birthday party for employees and an announcement that a $60,000 blood auto-analyzer had been ordered to increase the number of tests that could be made from one blood sample and cut the waiting period for results. Posters were placed strategically around the hospital inviting visitors to share in the celebration. The following month, the Governing Board and administrators hosted a hospital-wide family picnic at Springlake Amusement Park.

Also in 1969, Dr. Nazih Zuhdi performed the state's first Aorto-Coronary Bypass Graft and the first Internal Mammary Artery Coronary Artery Bypass Graft. Upon Zuhdi's arrival at BMC, he already was recognized worldwide as a leader and a teacher in cardiac surgery. He was a co-pioneer of the *stabilized* version of the glutaraldehyde porcine aortic valve, which was used in open-heart surgery for the first time in the world at Baptist.

In 1971, Dr. Lackey, whose vision of the hospital had been critical to its construction, retired as Executive Director-Treasurer of the Baptist General Convention of Oklahoma. Succeeding him was Dr. Joe L. Ingram, Lackey's second-in-command for a decade. Ingram's management style was slightly different that his mentor. Ingram was less interested in the day-to-day operation of the hospital than the overall concept of managing what had become one of the largest employers in the city.

In July, 1972, the organizational and management system was changed. Also, to reflect the comprehensive nature of services provided in various buildings on the campus, the official name of the facility was changed to Baptist Medical Center (BMC), although a new logo to announce the change was not unveiled until the next phase of construction was dedicated. Thanks to generous support of the Volunteer Auxiliary, the Children's World daycare opened in a new building on the corner of Northwest 54th Street and Independence Avenue.

The new trend of strategic planning instituted in the late 1960s bore immediate fruit. BMC leaders called for Phase III expansion, a $22.5 million project to add an East Tower with six floors, a North Tower with three floors of specialty care units, a two-level parking garage and additional space for support

Officials and employees gather to formally dedicate the East Tower in 1974.

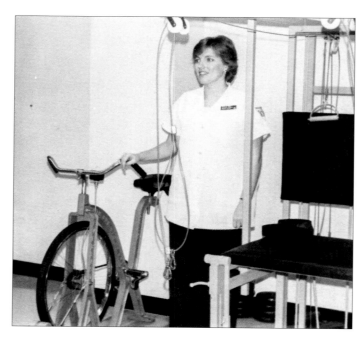

In November, 1975, an outpatient physical therapy unit opened. Physical therapist Phyllis Jones shows new equipment to visitors.

As the number of employees increased after the advent of Medicare, Baptist Medical Center bused workers from the east parking lot to the hospital.

services and equipment. Employee Boosters, an organization of hospital employees, raised $60,000 to construct a new landscaped plaza area adjacent to the hospital cafeteria.

In May, 1974, an open house was the setting for the dedication of Phase III. The hospital had grown to 563 beds and 40 percent of the original facility was renovated. The number of patient contacts in the first 15 years of the hospital's existence was staggering. The workforce had grown to 1,557 and 17,352 patient admissions were recorded.

Three new treatment centers opened in 1975. The Speech Pathology Department was created, a Gastrointestinal Laboratory opened, and the Baptist Burn Center, under the leadership of Dr. Paul Silverstein, opened with 11 beds to care for burn victims, filling a critical health care void for residents of Oklahoma. The full history of the Burn Center is found in Chapter Six.

The following year, the Cardiac Rehabilitation Unit was created, the Medical Oncology Unit opened, the School for Certified Respiratory Therapy Technicians was created, the helicopter landing pad was completed, and doctors marveled at the arrival of a CAT-scan machine. CAT stood for "Total Body Computed Tomography Scanner."

The Baptist Medical Center administration encouraged support for the community through United Appeal's annual campaign. Jerry Moeller, left, and Randy Segler were "coaches" for the 1976 campaign. Moeller is now CEO of Stillwater Medical Center and Segler is CEO of Comanche County Memorial Hospital in Lawton.

Baptist Medical Center's Obstetrics Department was one of the most popular in Oklahoma. A young family looks at their newest addition at the viewing window.

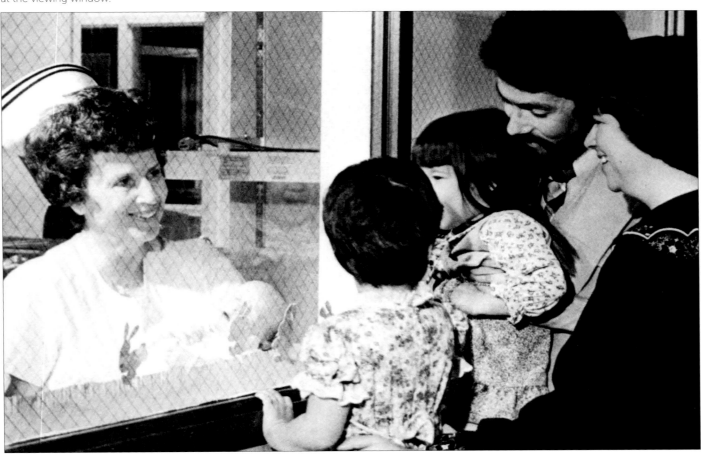

Courtesy Axiz Photography and Toby Nabors

CHAPTER 4

A Change In Direction

By 1977,
Baptist church leaders in Oklahoma were
concerned about continuing their role
of owning and operating hospitals.
The introduction of Medicare, massive
government red tape, and the spiraling
cost of health care had caused the
Baptist General Convention to re-think
hospital ownership.

The uneasiness of owning hospitals was forced to the forefront on September 16, 1977, with a headline on the front page of the *Oklahoma City Times* –CITY IS SEX CHANGE CENTER. Reporters had discovered that for a decade Baptist Medical Center had been one of the largest centers for sex change operations west of the Mississippi River. It trailed only Stanford University in California in the number of sex change procedures. Dr. David Foerster, a plastic surgeon who pioneered sex change surgery at BMC, admitted that about 50 such procedures had been completed. He was assisted in many of the operations by urologist, Dr. Charles Reynolds.

The public outcry was long and loud. Those for and against allowing sex change operations debated and re-debated the issue. When the Executive Committee of the Medical Staff and select members of the Governing Board voted to allow the operations to continue on a limited basis, Baptist General Convention Executive Director Dr. Joe Ingram said, "No." Administrator Jay Henry said, "It was the first time in my memory that the Baptist Convention overruled the hospital's Governing Board." It was apparent to all that the Governing Board was not legally in control of the hospital.

Within a short time, directors of the Baptist General Convention voted 54-2 to prohibit future transsexual operations at BMC. Ingram and Henry, both reasonable leaders, came to the mutual conclusion that it was time for the Baptist Convention to divest itself of the hospital. In a telephone call, Dr. Ingram said, "It's time," and gave Henry the authority to pursue such an arrangement.

In the final months of 1977, lawyers and financial experts began the detailed process of transferring ownership of the hospital to a new non-profit corporation, Oklahoma Healthcare Corporation.

There were three conditions under which Baptist leaders would allow the name "Baptist" to be retained in the name of the medical center. The first condition required that 60 percent, or 30, of the 50 directors of the new corporation be appointed from churches affiliated with the Baptist General Convention of Oklahoma. The second condition was a ban on sex change operations. A third condition was a restriction on abortions on demand. Abortions could be performed only in the event of an emergency when the mother's life was in danger. The contract for the transfer of the hospital stated that if, in the future, the word, "Baptist," was no longer used, none of the conditions would apply.

In June, 1978, ownership of BMC was transferred at a meeting of lawyers and representatives in New York City. The Baptist General Convention turned over its equity of $12.5 million in exchange for the agreement of the new corporation to pay back $27 million in outstanding hospital bonds used in recent expansion projects.

The new name of the hospital was officially changed to Baptist Medical Center of Oklahoma. The Restructuring Plan called for an expanded management team, headed by Administrator Henry who became President of the new entity. He was joined by Wilson Stinnett as Vice President for Operations and Dr. F.H. McGregor as Vice President for Medical Staff Affairs. A two-hospital concept was approved, with a separate administrator for the West and East towers. Betty Ware was named director of a new Central Nursing Service Department.

R.C. Howard, Jr., the chairman of the Governing Board, said, "The restructuring is the result of long and careful study and consultation with management experts. It places emphasis of attention even more squarely on patient care."

The gender change controversy caused Chief of Staff Bennett to reconsider by-laws of the Medical Staff and credentialing of doctors at the hospital. Judy Hoisington was elevated to assistant administrator and handled credentialing. Not only did the hospital have strict by-laws in regard to allowing doctors to practice, but each clinical department developed additional rules and regulations limiting doctors in performance of procedures related to their board certification.

In addition to the new ownership of the hospital, the Baptist Medical Center of Oklahoma Foundation, Inc., was created in 1978. The charitable non-profit corporation was organized to manage funds contributed in support of BMC. The Foundation's purpose was to attract philanthropy to sustain and support BMC in providing the utmost in quality health services. President Henry said, "The Foundation will help assure continuing excellence of the services of Baptist Medical Center by participating in the planning and development of goals for future growth and obtaining financial support necessary for their realization."

ProHealth was also established in 1978 as a for-profit entity to provide managerial services to other area health care facilities. The new group took over some operations of hospitals in Seminole, Eufaula, Holdenville, Enid, and Clinton. Medicol was created to provide collection services for hospitals and physicians.

The PACER Fitness Center opened in November, 1978. It was a new facility for cardiac rehabilitation and aerobic conditioning. PACER, the first fitness center of its kind attached to a hospital, was an outgrowth of BMC's Cardiac Rehabilitation Unit to help coronary patients return to a normal lifestyle after surgery. PACER was an acronym for Prevention of Atherosclerosis and Coronary disease through Education and Rehabilitation. PACER Associates, a group of physicians and health care professionals, operated the center in connection with BMC. *Apollo 15* astronaut Jim Irwin was the guest during grand opening ceremonies for PACER on November 19.

The PACER facilities included indoor and outdoor running tracks, treadmills, bicycle ergometers, gym equipment, whirlpools, saunas, showers, lockers, emergency resuscitation equipment, classrooms, and a juice bar. The fitness center was also open to employees and the general public for a nominal monthly charge.

PACER offered far more services than a gym or spa. Prior to a client initiating an exercise program, a battery of medical and fitness tests were required. The tests provided the information essential to individual problem identification and the design of a proper, safe exercise program.

As BMC grew in stature, innovations of many kinds emerged. A significant event was the establishment of the Cochlear Implant Clinic, one of the first such centers in the nation approved by the Food and Drug Administration. The clinic was the result of

In 1978, world renowned microscopic ear surgeon Dr. Jack Van Doren Hough founded what later became the Hough Ear Institute at Baptist Medical Center.

With the development of the cochlear ear implant, Dr. Jack Van Doren Hough and Baptist Medical Center were at the cutting edge of treatment of the deaf.

BAPTIST MEDICAL CENTER

WINTER 1980

HEALTH SIGNS

Burn Care: The reach toward recovery

The Baptist Burn Center was featured on the cover of the Winter, 1980 issue of *Baptist Medical Center Health Signs*.

the work of Dr. Jack Van Doren Hough, a pioneer ear surgeon, who had been conducting surgery of the middle ear with the aid of a microscope. Because small nerve endings make up the electrical system of the middle ear, Hough believed that a multidisciplinary team of physicians, including specialists in electrical engineering and neurophysiology, would be necessary to develop a new generation of help for totally deaf people.

In 1978, Hough established what later became the Hough Ear Institute. His desire was to conduct research and development for cochlear implants for those who had profound and total deafness, implantable devices for nerve and conductive deafness, and standard hearing aids, especially in poorer countries around the globe. The complete history of the Hough Ear Institute can be found in Chapter Eleven.

The year 1978 was also significant for other innovations at the hospital. The Ambulatory Surgical Unit, providing alternative care for minor surgery procedures, was created. Oklahoma's first statewide diagnostic network, the Telephonic EEG Network, allowed remote evaluation and diagnosis for residents in outlying sections of the state. BMC also established a television production studio to assist in continuing education for staff and employees and for videotaping surgeries for physicians. In addition, the Pastoral Care Department was officially accredited as a Clinical Pastoral Education Center, beginning the process of training hundreds of chaplains, pastors, and pastoral counselors in the decades since the Center's inception.

Ken Bonds was an active chairman of the Governing Board in the late 1970s. He predicted that the hospital business would become similar to the banking and grocery industries. Small "mom and pop" or family-owned institutions were diminishing in number, and larger, more efficient units were taking their place. Bonds said, "The law of economics applies. Hospitals will have to think in terms of increasing market share just like any other business."

In 1979, Baptist Medical Center celebrated its 20th anniversary. Five employees remained from the first day of operation of the hospital—President Jay Henry, comptroller Sturgis Cashon, secretary Dee Kerns, engineer Joe Melendez, and housekeeper Iva Warlick.

By 1980, BMC's performance had secured its prominent position in medical care in the state. The medical/dental staff exceeded 300 and the total number of employees was more than 1,800. The campus had come a long way—from a single tower to five structures. With an increase in population

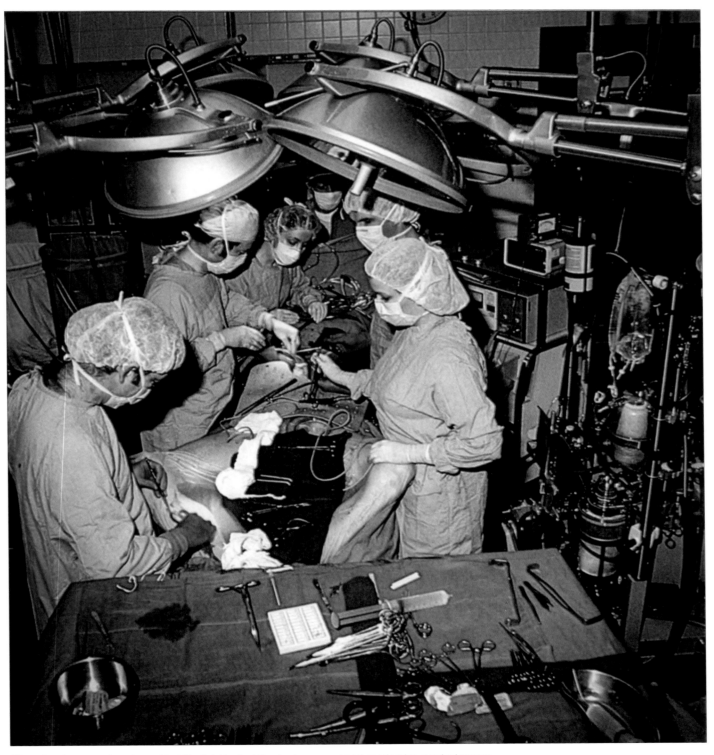

The sale of revenue bonds enabled Baptist Medical Center to expand and modernize surgical rooms.

In 1980, Louis Yarzab, left, was the first recipient of the Infusaid pump in Oklahoma, a new way to provide concentrated chemical therapy. Yarzab learns about the new device from nurse Emily Fuller. *Courtesy Oklahoma Publishing Company.*

in Oklahoma, administrators began serious efforts to expand the physical plant with an eye on the fast-moving technological changes that were happening in the hospital industry and in life in general.

Digital Subtraction Angiography, a system to detect blockage of blood vessels and clots, was offered on an outpatient basis. A CT scanner allowed doctors to perform diagnostic tests in a painless and non-invasive manner. UltraSound, another non-invasive tool, and four gamma cameras that tracked radioactive materials within a specific portion of the body were used. A gamma camera, hooked to an EKG machine, could take "pictures" of the heart in motion.

The oncology program developed quickly. Dr. James Hampton began oncology treatment on a wider scale when he arrived from the Oklahoma Medical Research Foundation in 1979. The following year, Dr. Karl K. Boatman led a surgical team in implanting a pump in a patient with severe liver disease that transmitted precise amounts of chemical therapy. The Infusaid pump delivered therapy that was 100 to 400 times more concentrated than previous therapy. A complete history of Baptist's oncology program is found in Chapter Ten.

The LDR concept for birth mothers was pioneered at BMC in 1980. It allowed mothers their first opportunity for Labor-Delivery-and-Recovery all in the same room that took on the appearance of a bedroom in their home. The Women's Health Center soon added a state-of-the-art Neonatal Unit to provide service to premature babies.

In 1981, Dr. Thomas N. Lynn, Jr., became BMC's first Vice President of Medical and Scientific Affairs, emphasizing the administration's continued commitment to conducting research. Ultimately, the private, not-for-profit group, the Institute for Health Care Research, was renamed the Thomas N. Lynn Institute for Health Care Research.

In January, 1982, an updated Pediatric Unit opened. Clowns, balloons, and nurses dressed in animal costumes paraded down the south hall of Ten West to show off the complete remodeling of the pediatric and young adult units. New carpets, drapes, wallpaper, and decorations were designed especially for young patients. Head Nurse Joy Jones said, "If decorating is appealing, it stimulates continued growing and recovery of the child." The pediatric intensive care nursery was totally renovated and contained five cribs enclosed in individual cubicles. Windows permitted continuous observation by doctors and family members.

In 1981, Oklahoma City attorney James Paul "Jimmy" Linn and his wife, Ann, made a donation

to the hospital to complete a three-floor addition to the Special Care Tower named in his honor. The BMC volunteer program expanded in numbers and mission. Not only did volunteers give thousands of hours each month to provide much-needed services to patients, they contributed large sums of money to assist in programs at the hospital.

The Baptist Alternate Birth Environment "BABE" was a two-room suite in the Labor and Delivery area where family members could participate in the birth experience.

BAPTIST "FIRSTS" IN THE 1980s

1980
- Dr. Karl Boatman leads team to implant infusion pump, launching intensive oncology program

1982
- Oklahoma's first hospital to have accredited Hospital Pharmacy Residency

1983
- Hospital becomes part of Oklahoma Healthcare Corporation
- First cochlear implant on a child performed by Dr. Jack Van Doren Hough
- Oklahoma Heart Center founded—the hospital's first Center of Excellence

1984
- Oklahoma Transplant Institute founded by Dr. Nazih Zuhdi

1985
- Oklahoma's first heart transplant performed by Dr. Nazih Zuhdi
- Cancer Center of the Southwest opens
- Oklahoma's first piggyback heart transplant performed by Dr. Nazih Zuhdi

1986
- Henry G. Bennett, Jr. Fertility Institute opens
- Baptist Laser Institute opens, first in Oklahoma
- The Baptist Medical Plaza, now Building B, opens
- Third Age Life Center opens to inform public of senior health care issues

1987
- First kidney transplant performed by Dr. Scott Samara
- Oklahoma's first heart-lung transplant by team led by Dr. Nazih Zuhdi

1988
- First hospital in Oklahoma to be granted permission to implant ventricular assist devices to prolong life for patients awaiting transplant surgery
- Doctors Nazih Zuhdi and Dimitri Novitzky led the implantation of a left and right ventricular assist device, approved weeks later by the Food and Drug Administration

1989
- First hospital in Oklahoma, and first non-teaching hospital in nation, to be approved by Medicare for transplants
- Sleep Diagnostic and Research Center opens

The PACER Fitness Center has been an award-winning program for decades, focusing on individualized attention for maximum benefit.

Oklahoma Supreme Court Justice Robert A. Hefner notes a plaque honoring his family for donations made to Baptist Medical Center.

Oklahoma City attorney Jimmy Linn donated substantial funds in 1981 to complete an addition to the Special Care Tower.

Dr. Thomas N. Lynn, Jr., left, with Dr. Paul Silverstein. Lynn was named Baptist Medical Center's first Vice President of Medical and Scientific Affairs in 1981. He previously served for many years as dean of the University of Oklahoma College of Medicine.

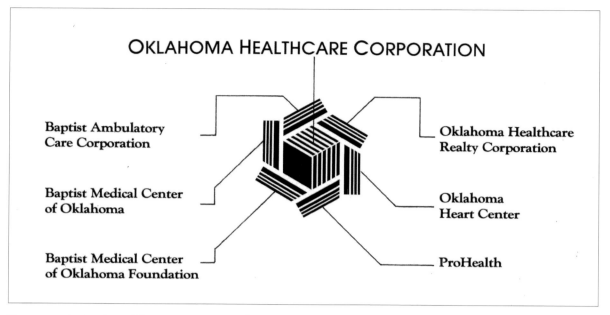

The corporate structure of the parent company of Baptist Medical Center after changes in 1983.

Leaders of Baptist Medical Center in 1984. Front row, left to right, Dr. Thomas N. Lynn, vice president; B. Eugene McPherson, vice president; and Carolyn B. Jones, vice president, Baptist Medical Center of Oklahoma Foundation. Second row, Philip Newbold, vice president; Barrett Evans, director of planning, John Plyler, Jr., executive vice president; Daniel E. Short, executive vice president, Oklahoma Heart Center; and Jerrold A. Maki, vice president. Back row, Thomas E. Payne, vice president; Marvin Pember, controller; and Maureen G. Byrnes, vice president.

Nurse Danette Wheeler demonstratives intensive care heart monitoring equipment maintained by Baptist Medical Center's Clinical Engineering Department in 1984.

In the 1980s, home health care services of Baptist Medical Center allowed patients to enjoy the comforts of their own home.

Hugga T. Bear gives hugs of all kinds at Children's World. The bear was introduced as the hospital mascot to promote friendship and love through hugs.

Volunteers have always been an integral part of patient care at Baptist Medical Center. Volunteers support staff with a wide variety of activities, including staffing the Surgery Waiting Room.

After corporate reorganization in 1985, Jay Henry, left, was president of Oklahoma Healthcare Corporation, Ken Bonds was chairman of the corporation's Board of Directors, and Philip Newbold was president of Baptist Medical Center of Oklahoma, Inc.

In 1983, another restructuring of the corporate framework of Baptist Medical Center occurred. Jay Henry became president of Oklahoma Healthcare Corporation (OHC) and Phillip A. Newbold, a BMC vice president, was elevated to president of the medical center. Placed under the new OHC umbrella were subsidiaries Oklahoma Ambulatory Care, Oklahoma Healthcare Realty Corporation, and the Oklahoma Heart Center, Inc. An Administrative Cabinet of nine vice presidents was formed. Members included Dr. Thomas Lynn, B. Eugene McPherson, Carolyn B. Jones, Barrett G. Evans, Daniel E. Short, Jerrold A. Maki, Thomas E. Payne, Marvin Pember, and Maureen G. Byrnes.

The following year, BMC became a shareholder in Voluntary Hospitals of America, Inc., a nationwide group of non-profit hospitals, that joined forces to seek cost reductions through group purchasing arrangements.

BMC marked its 25th anniversary in 1984 with a week-long schedule of events. Governor George Nigh proclaimed April 25th "Baptist Medical Center Day." More than 400 employees displayed arts and crafts. The celebration finale was the release of hundreds of balloons by employees who circled the hospital.

The Oklahoma Heart Center was founded in 1984 by Dr. Nazih Zuhdi, chairman; Dr. Ronald White, president; and Dr. John J. Donnell. The Heart Center was named BMC's first Center of Excellence. Its complete history is found in Chapter Seven. Dr. Zuhdi previously performed years of research at Mercy Hospital and founded the Oklahoma Cardiovascular Institute at St. Anthony Hospital. Dr. Zuhdi moved his talents to BMC where he saw the establishment of the Oklahoma Heart Center as simply the first step in a larger vision. The unique story of Dr. Zuhdi's arrival at BMC is told in Chapter Ten. Zuhdi's biographer, Brooks Barr, wrote:

> Nazih Zuhdi would not be content with a monolithic heart center; he wanted it to be a vehicle for concepts, education, research, discoveries, and transplantation—a center that could stand toe-to-toe and heart-to-heart with any center in the world.

Dr. J. Hartwell Dunn speaks to fellow members of the Medical Staff at the 25th anniversary of Baptist Medical Center in 1984.

Because of a desire to strengthen its position in the area of women's and children's services, Baptist Medical Center expanded pediatric services in the mid-1980s.

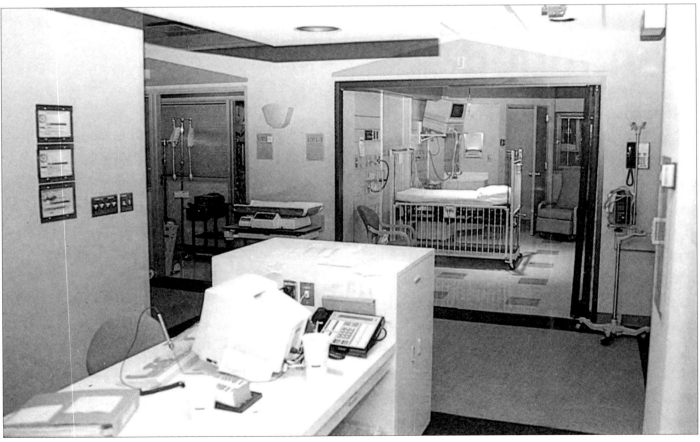

Plans were approved in 1985 for the construction of the Doctor's Medical Plaza.

The creation of the Oklahoma Heart Center began to put BMC on the medical map in the Southwest. Dr. Zuhdi's idea for a multi-discipline heart program of national and international importance did not come easy. Many of Zuhdi's fellow physicians grumbled. But others, such as Dr. J. Hartwell Dunn and Dr. Bobby Gene Smith, encouraged Zuhdi to continue his quest for excellence.

The administration of BMC was hesitant to launch into the new frontier of innovative treatments for heart disease, including Oklahoma's first heart transplant. But, BMC board chairman Ken Bonds believed in Dr. Zuhdi and authorized him to staff the Oklahoma Heart Center to ensure the quality of envisioned services. Zuhdi enlisted the help of his former colleague, Dr. Christiaan Barnard, the surgeon who performed the world's first human heart transplant, in a vigorous public relations campaign to "sell" the people of Oklahoma about the importance of this new direction of BMC that, frankly, would move the hospital to a position of medical excellence of which few had dreamed.

Dr. Zuhdi changed his base for future organ transplants when he created the Oklahoma Transplant Institute in 1984 and served as chairman and Surgeon-in-Chief. Again, the road was difficult. While the administration sometimes balked at Zuhdi's fast timeline of achievement, Bonds and a handful of fellow physicians supported his vision. Often, Zuhdi was frustrated—he twice resigned. But, his dream for BMC to be the center of the emerging world of heart and other organ transplants brought him quickly back. Dr. Thomas Lynn remembered, "Often the hospital administration did not know what Zuhdi was doing. It was Zuhdi's program, and his *alone*."

The story of Oklahoma's first human heart transplant in 1985 and the world-recognized significance of the transplant program at BMC is found in Chapter Ten.

With the celebration of the hospital's 25 years of service to the community, a special era ended. Dr. Henry G. Bennett, Jr., the first and only Chief of Staff of BMC, died in December, 1984. Gloria Howe Bremkamp wrote:

> A good listener, a thoughtful man, he was a person capable of giving fair consideration to difficult questions. And though he was a peacemaker at heart, he could stand unflinchingly in the center of controversy. As a result of these traits of strength, his legacy of leadership was one of stability that remains.

Dr. Bennett was replaced as Chief of the Medical and Dental Staff by Dr. H. Thompson Avey. After

Dr. Nazhi Zuhdi, left, and Baptist Medical Center board chairman Ken Bonds. Bonds backed efforts to establish a world-renowned heart treatment center, even over the objections of members of the board and the hospital's administration. "Without Ken Bonds," Dr. Zuhdi said, "our world-class cardiac treatment and transplant program, including liver, pancreas, and intestines, would not have occurred at Baptist Medical Center. He was essential to its success." *Courtesy Oklahoma Publishing Company.*

several years in the position, Dr. Avey was succeeded by Dr. William E. Hood, Jr., as Chief of Staff.

In 1985, the first cancer treatment center in Oklahoma was formed as the Cancer Center of the Southwest. Dr. James W. Hampton was Medical Director of the Center that was designed as a Center of Excellence. Its complete story is found in Chapter Ten. Dr. Jack Van Doren Hough performed Baptist's first cochlear implant on a child, the first in the state and one of the first in the nation. Baptist Care Advantage, a home health service, began providing care to patients in their homes.

Also in 1985, the Good Food Bakery was opened, the Osteoporosis Center was established, the first piggy back heart transplant was performed, and the first 22-channel cochlear implant surgery was performed.

Another major endeavor was unveiled in 1986 with the opening of the Henry G. Bennett, Jr. Fertility Institute. Dr. David A. Kallenberger was Medical Director. The story of the Bennett Fertility Institute is found in Chapter Twelve.

More innovative programs appeared in 1986. Dr. Royice Everett opened the Baptist Laser Institute, the first of its kind in the state. The Third Age Life Center was founded to offer education and assessment of needs for seniors in the community. The first 24-hour pharmacokinetics service in Oklahoma began

The changing skyline of Baptist Medical Center following completion of Phase IV construction in 1986.

in the hospital's pharmacy department. The program allowed staff to mathematically tailor a drug dosage for patients by measuring blood levels before and after the medication was administered.

The Baptist Medical Plaza, now known as Building B, opened in October, 1986, with space for 53 physician offices. The building was a joint effort of the BMC and Baptist Medical Plaza Associates LTD, a group of physicians that participated in construction costs. An open house was held on October 5 to show visitors the new facilities that included the Medical Plaza Surgery Center, the Cardiovascular Laboratory, the Bennett Fertility Institute, the Medical Plaza Hotel, and radiology services.

In June, 1986, Jay Henry announced his plans to retire after guiding the hospital through more than 25 years of incredible growth. In announcing Henry's retirement, Board of Directors Chairman Ken Bonds said:

> Jay Henry goes beyond managing. Utilizing exceptional skills as a visionary leader, he has always looked at 5-year, 10-year segments of our growth and development. But no man, however capable and gifted, works in a void. His greatest talent has been the ability to surrounded himself with excellent staff. As Baptist moved into big-time health care, he had the foresight to attract outstanding lieutenants, thus demonstrating the ultimate abilities of the true leader.

On December 5, the hospital's Board of Directors hosted a black-tie dinner in Henry's honor at the Marriott Hotel. In appreciation for his many fine years of service, Henry was invited to serve on the Board of Directors which launched a nationwide search for his successor.

Before Henry turned over the reins of the medical center, he and the Board of Directors began to plan for further expansion. Needs identified were the correction of functional deficiencies of the West Tower, increasing the number of private rooms from 56 percent to 65 percent, and increasing the total number of hospital beds from 507 to 577.

A new outpatient atrium and lobby were created in the 1986 expansion.

Courtesy Axiz Photography and Toby Nabors

CHAPTER 5

New Leadership—
New Direction

Change in healthcare delivery in America was moving at breakneck speed as the Board of Directors considered Jay Henry's replacement. At monthly meetings, Board Chairman Ken Bonds led discussions of what the group was looking for in a new head of the medical center's parent company. Henry suggested the name of Stanley E. "Stan" Hupfeld, head of All Saints Episcopal Hospital in Fort Worth, Texas. Henry had known Hupfeld through their membership in various hospital associations

Baptist Medical Center purchased the Physicians Professional Building west of the hospital in 1987. *Courtesy Gary Payne.*

When first contacted about the Baptist job, Hupfeld was uncertain about his ability to "be a fit." He was a Catholic and a member of the 1963 national championship football team at the University of Texas. He was aware that BMC had a strong Baptist background and that many Oklahoma football fans strongly disliked the Texas Longhorns.

Bonds and other board members appreciated Hupfeld, not only for his obvious expertise in running a large medical facility, but for his civic involvement. Bonds said, "Right away, we knew he was the man for the job. We quickly got over the fact that he was Catholic and that he was a Longhorn." Bonds believed that Hupfeld's professional experience was ideal for long-range plans that needed to be developed quickly to meet BMC's growing mission.

Hupfeld, who was hired as president and chief executive officer effective April 1, 1987, was raised in Dallas, served in Germany and Vietnam as an officer in the Army Medical Corps, and earned a master's degree in hospital administration from Trinity University in San Antonio, Texas. One of his first efforts was to pull together representatives from all organizations within the sprawling BMC complex to develop a strategic financial plan for the future. The result of extensive discussions was the identification of $100 million in capital needs. BMC embarked on a multi-phased construction program designed to bring the complex into the next century.

As details of future expansions developed, other "firsts" for the hospital occurred. The Rehabilitation Services department was created. Dr. E.N. "Scott" Samara performed the first kidney transplant in the Oklahoma Transplant Institute and Dr. Nazih Zuhdi performed the state's first heart-lung transplant, assisted by Dr. David K.C. Cooper and Dr. Dimitri Novitzky. Dr. Zuhdi recruited Cooper and Novitzky from South Africa where they trained under Dr. Christiaan Barnard, heart transplant pioneer.

In 1987, the Raymond A. Young Conference Center and the 263-seat James L. Henry Auditorium were completed. Three additional conference rooms and a full-service catering department enhanced the medical center's ability to accommodate large groups and seminars. BMC opened the first of several Primary Care Centers in the metropolitan area to provide convenient access for patients to physicians and primary health care services. In 1988, the Meridian Occupational Health Center was opened to provide emergency care for work-related injuries.

The silver, mirrored glass office building immediately west of the main hospital, built by Dr. Edward M. Farris in 1973, was purchased by the medical center in 1987. The building had been constructed on land occupied by the Highland Hills Baptist Church at the corner of Grand Boulevard and the Northwest Highway. At the time, Grand was merely a dirt trail. The original name of the building was Physicians Professional Building. The new building was of advanced design. It included hermetically sealed walls, Westinghouse elevators, and modern air conditioning and heating.

Hupfeld was heavily engaged in civic activities and encouraged members of his management team to be involved in the community also. Hupfeld said, "As medical organizations grow and expand their business interests to include pharmacies, clinics, and other enterprises, it becomes increasingly important for a chief executive officer to have substantial contact with the community."

Hupfeld's assistant administrator, Judy Hoisington, said, "Stan's absolute dedication to community involvement made him the most visionary person I ever worked with. He always was excited about new projects that would allow the medical center to give back to the community that had supported the hospital for so many years."

In 1988, BMC was one of only 24 medical centers nationwide to receive Medicare approval for its heart transplant program. BMC was the first hospital in the state and the only non-teaching hospital in the United States to receive Medicare's approval. Newspapers referred to BMC as the "heart hub" of Oklahoma.

Also in 1988, the Food and Drug Administration approved Oklahoma as one of 20 states in which a left and right ventricular assist device could be used to take over the functions of both ventricles of the heart to maintain the patient's heart until a suitable donor heart could be found for a transplant. Dr. Zuhdi and Dr. Novitzky had used the device days before FDA approval to keep Mona Stevens alive. Stevens successful heart transplantation surgery was performed by Dr. Zuhdi a few months later.

Baptist Care Advantage was the first program in the state to offer continuous neonatal pulse oximetry monitoring and blood transfusions in the home. The Rehabilitation Unit at BMC became the first hospital-based unit in Oklahoma City to receive accreditation from the national accrediting body. The American Nursing Association accredited BMC as a Continuing Education provider because of implementation of a clinical career advancement program that provided financial recognition to registered nurses for giving excellent patient bedside care.

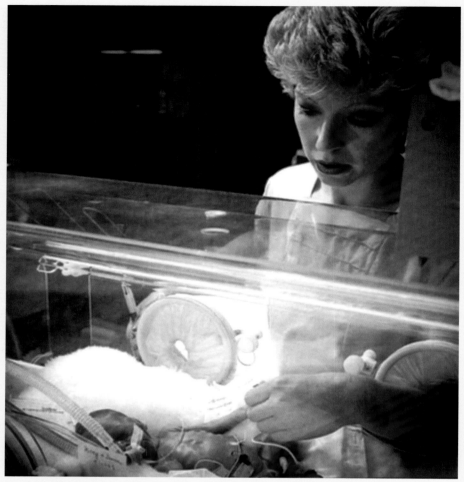

Nurse Kim DuChamp monitors the special needs of a neonatal baby in the Neonatal Intensive Care Unit at Baptist Medical Center in 1989.

MISSION STATEMENT OF THE OKLAHOMA HEALTHCARE CORPORATION IN 1990

"CARING FOR PEOPLE IS OUR FOUNDATION, OUR PURPOSE"

C Caring is respect for individuality and human potential.

A Caring is the commitment of all that we have, all that we are.

R Caring is responding to our community's needs with our talents and resources.

I Caring is the continual pursuit of quality and the expansion of knowledge.

N Caring is compassion for the whole person, every person.

G Caring is working together with dedication from the heart.

In 1989, the Sleep Diagnostic and Research Center opened to treat patients with sleep apnea and other sleep-disturbing health problems. The Center was directed by Dr. William C. Orr. The Sleep Diagnostic and Research Center story is found in Chapter Thirteen.

Building expansion included four more floors added to the East Tower. Other improvements included a renovated and expanded laboratory, a new Outpatient Department, and major renovations to the emergency room. Two large trauma rooms with X-ray capability within the room and the addition of a new nurses' station and registration area improved service to emergency patients.

In 1991, thanks to a $1.2 million gift of the Volunteer Auxiliary, the innovative daycare center, Children's World, changed its name to Children's Place and moved into a 13,000-square-foot building. The facility was awarded the highest rating for daycare centers in Oklahoma. The donation from the Volunteer Auxiliary was the latest in a long list of significant donations to the medical center from volunteers. Just in the 1980s, volunteers gave $750,000 to help construct new operating rooms, $800,000 for birth suite modification, and $100,000 for scholarship programs.

An expansion of the Baptist Women's Health Center created a state-of-the-art health care facility for women. The Center's medical director, Dr. Mary Ann Bauman, insisted that the scope of care was far beyond giving birth to babies. She said, "Important as it is, a woman's reproductive time is only a small portion of her total lifespan."

The Women's Center provided excellent care for giving birth. There were 22 labor-delivery-recovery-post-partum (LDRP) suites, 26 gynecology rooms, a 22-bed neonatal intensive care unit, and two surgical suites for cesarean-section deliveries.

Dr. Bauman and Linda Merkey, Division Director of Women's and Children's Services, oversaw a unit that cared for women with a variety of problems—breast biopsies, eye problems, chronic disease management, urinary incontinence, and hysterectomies. The Women's Center was seen as an umbrella over a variety of services.

The Women's Health Forum became a popular annual lecture series on women's health issues. The forum was jointly planned by BMC staffers and an advisory board composed of women from the community. Each year, the forum offers a series of seminars, free to the public, featuring medical experts and celebrities. Even in the early years of the forum, between 3,000 and 5,000 women attended seminars during the week-long event.

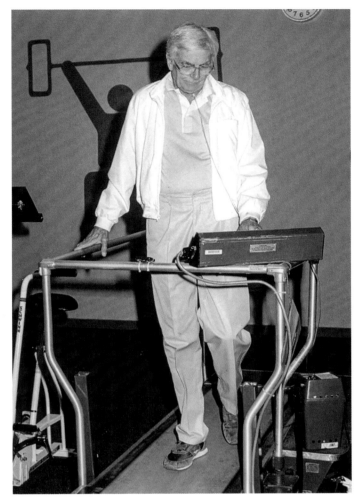

J.C. Burks, the actor who portrayed the Marlboro Man in early television commercials and print ads, was a patient in the pulmonary rehabilitation program. He walked on the treadmill two to three times each week at the PACER Fitness Center.

Dr. Scott Newton of the Baptist Care Center on North Pennsylvania in Oklahoma City discusses a treatment plan with a patient in 1989.

Longtime volunteer Alice Gaskins donated more than 12,000 hours in service to the hospital.

BMC President Stan Hupfeld was known for wearing many hats and costumes to generate interest among hospital employees in United Way and other community programs. Such dress-up events by senior management was the idea of special events director Sally Ritcheson Burks. They proved to be popular with employees. At various times, Hupfeld was dressed as Cher, Elvis, and Cinderella.

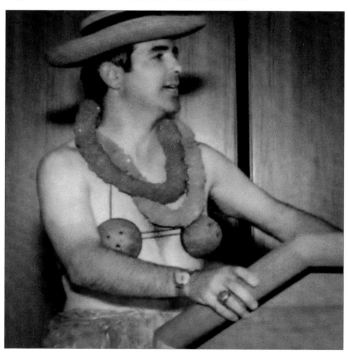

In addition to sponsoring the annual health forum, the Women's Health Center began an intensive program to take the message of good health care to the community. Dr. Bauman was a regular on local television. The Center's staff brought young women in from area high schools and talked to them about sexually transmitted diseases, pregnancies, drugs, lack of exercise, and other problems they would encounter as adults. In the "On Your Own" series, they also talked to the young women about managing relationships with boyfriends, bosses, and professors.

President Hupfeld unveiled a unique community project in 1992 called "Project 2000." It was a partnership with the Oklahoma City public school system. Employees from Baptist were trained to serve as mentors and role models to at-risk elementary school male students. The three-fold purpose of the program, a first for Oklahoma City, was to: (1) provide a needed community service to positively influence Oklahoma City children; (2) offer employees at BMC a rewarding opportunity; and (3) position BMC as a leader in community support activities.

In addition to the mentoring aspect of Project 2000, a scholarship fund was established by the Oklahoma Healthcare Corporation to provide annual scholarships for students to use later to help cover the costs of higher education. All mentoring was completed on school premises and was under the supervision of the school district. Men spent an average of two hours twice a week to provide classroom assistance for teachers. The project was renamed "Positive Directions" in 1993 when it received a special innovation award from Oklahoma Superintendent of Public Instruction Sandy Garrett. Positive Directions continues to offer assistance to at-risk students.

Another program instituted in the renewed effort to make BMC an integral part of the community was "Calm Waters," an outpatient counseling program for children who had suffered a loss of a parent or sibling. Now a separate, self sustaining program, Calm Waters has assisted more than 15,000 Oklahoma children.

BMC employees helped give back to the community in many ways. In May, 1994, 200 employees donated hundreds of hours of their time to build a Habitat for Humanity home on Northwest Seventh Street in Oklahoma City. Every department of the hospital participated in the building blitz. Also, employees of the engineering department solicited donations of supplies and materials from area businesses. Robin Hamilton-Folks, executive director of Central Oklahoma Habitat for Humanity, said, "The contribution of Baptist Medical Center employees was beyond our wildest expectations. Thanks to them, a family which otherwise could not afford it, has moved into a new home, away from the gang-infested project where they lived before."

Staff volunteers at BMC provided health screening for hundreds of central Oklahoma children and their parents at Penn Square Mall each year for the Kid Care program. Doctors and nurses from the hospital and a dozen local dentists volunteered their time to screen for potential medical problems.

A unique fundraising program to benefit the Emergency Department in 1993 was the Baptist Bungee Jump. For $95 each, participants could be hoisted six stories above the ground on a crane being used for hospital campus construction. John Safety, director of Baptist Medical Center Security, oversaw security for the bungee jump.

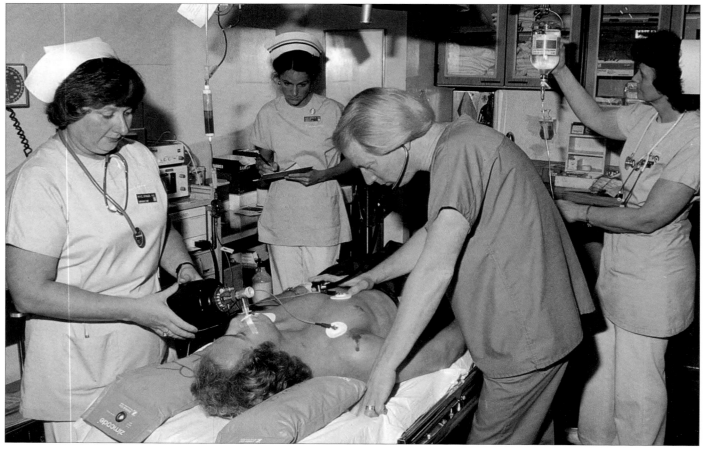

The strategic location of Baptist Medical Center gave emergency room nurses many opportunities to prove their fast, efficient care to multiple trauma patients.

In 1993, BMC opened the Baptist Community Clinic at the Olivet Baptist Church on Northwest Tenth Street. BMC volunteers gathered three times each month to deliver medical treatment to patients from the surrounding neighborhoods. Physicians, nurses, dental hygienists, audiologists, dietitians, pharmacists, and other specialists saw everything from rashes to heart disease, and broken bones to diabetes. Lyn Hester, director of BMC's community development department, said in 1994, "We give immunizations, pregnancy tests and check for blood sugar. Anyone who needs lab work, X-rays, or even surgery is treated at no cost." The program received the Award for Volunteer Excellence from the American Hospital Association in 1994.

Stan Hupfeld congratulates mentors in the award-winning Positive Directions program. Left to right, Clay Rivers, Marvin King, Hupfeld, Ed Hamilton, and Kenneth Peoples.

A button helped celebrated a time of remembering the quarter century of contributions of Jay Henry.

James L. Henry WEEK

Baptist Medical Center employees built a Habitat for Humanity home in 1994, part of the hospital's community involvement.

Nursing services has always been an indispensable part of patient services at Baptist Medical Center. Brenda Vanzandt, left, Director of Nursing in the West Tower and Betty Hudson, Director of Nursing in the East Tower.

BAPTIST "FIRSTS" IN THE 1990s

1990
- Board of Directors approves a "tithing" commitment to fund community service programs such as free health screening, free immunizations, and an educational lecture series

1991
- An annual Women's Health Forum begins
- First liver transplant performed by Dr. Luis Mieles

1992
- Project 2000, later renamed Positive Directions, is launched to mentor at-risk public school students

1993
- The Baptist Community Clinic opens at Olivet Baptist Church
- Oklahoma's first liver-kidney transplant is performed by Dr. Hadar Merhav and Dr. Scott Samara

1994
- Cancer Center of the Southwest becomes Troy & Dollie Smith Cancer Center
- First double lung transplant performed by Dr. Nazih Zuhdi

1995
- The Hyperbaric Medicine and Wound Care Center opens, a first for Oklahoma
- Pediatric Intensive Care Unit opens
- Oklahoma's first live-donor liver transplant and nation's first in-situ split liver transplant

1998
- The James L. Hall Jr. Center for Mind, Body and Spirit opens, the first of its kind in Oklahoma

Country music star Naomi Judd, right, and Dr. Mary Ann Baumann at the Women's Health Forum in 1993.

Drawing on facing page: In 1992, the Oklahoma Healthcare Corporation approved expansion plans for a new medical office building and a six-story parking garage. The eight-story building provided consolidated facilities for the Cancer Center of the Southwest and office space for 70 physicians.

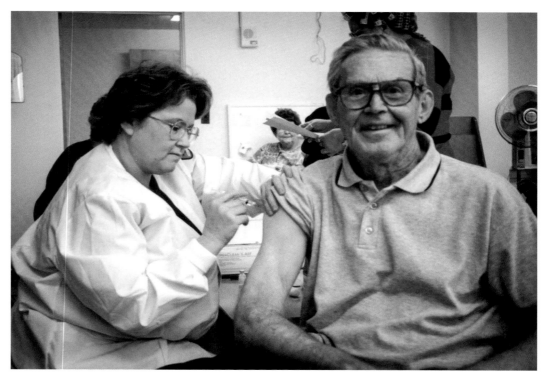

A patient receives an injection as part of the free medical service at the Baptist Community Clinic.

Also in 1994, Oklahoma Healthcare Corporation expanded its horizons beyond Baptist Medical Center. The idea for a statewide network of hospitals was conceived by President Hupfeld and Dr. Joe L. Ingram, president of Baptist Healthcare of Oklahoma, Inc., that owned 14 hospitals in rural Oklahoma located in Blackwell, Bristow, Drumright, Enid, Grove, Guthrie, Guymon, Hugo, Madill, Miami, Pawnee, Pryor, Stroud, and Watonga.

Before the new system could be created, Dr. Ingram died. But, led by Hupfeld, the parties continued negotiations and the original hospitals operated by the Baptist General Convention were together again. The agreements resulted in the creation of the statewide Oklahoma Health System and central management of BMC and 13 rural hospitals. The following year, Oklahoma Healthcare entered into an agreement with Southwest Medical Center in Oklahoma City which became part of the system. Southwest Medical Center was formerly South Community Hospital. Hupfeld served as president of the reconfigured organization.

Harold Stansberry, an original member of the board of directors at INTEGRIS Southwest Medical Center, and chairman of the INTEGRIS Foundation, was honored in 1995. Left to right, Stan Hupfeld, Stansberry, and Frank McPherson.

Even though the demands of healthcare reform in the United States brought about the mergers, each hospital continued to operate with its own administration and board of directors. Combined, the hospitals had 1,705 licensed beds, 1,318 physicians, and net annual revenues of $366 million.

Shortly after the new corporate management structure was announced, BMC leaders asked Oklahoma County commissioners to approve a bond issue to refinance higher-rate bonds from previous expansion and to make substantial new capital expenditures. In December, 1993, the Oklahoma Industries Authority authorized issuance of up to $215 million in revenue bonds for hospital projects.

Karen Miller, Director of Corporate Planning, outlined an immediate $21 million project to fund 10 new operating rooms, a new hyperbaric area for the Burn Center, a new electrical vault at the north end of the physicians' parking area, a new boiler plant, a 700-car parking garage, and an eight-story medical office building. The expansion allowed for renovation of all surgical suites, a tripling in size of post-anesthesia recovery, ambulatory surgery, and other holding spaces.

As with all phases of construction of the hospital, management looked to the community for private donations. In 1992, the Circles of Excellence donor

recognition program was created by the Baptist Medical Center Foundation to honor individuals, corporations, organizations, and foundations that made a substantial investment in the hospital. An annual system-wide dinner spotlights winners in a number of categories including, a Foundation Partnership Award, Corporate Partnership Award, Volunteer Leadership Award, and a Young Philanthropist Award.

In 1994, BMC unveiled a telemedicine network that allowed a specialist at the hospital to review X-rays, hear a patient's heart, and observe the patient at a remote location. Hospitals on the telemedicine network included institutions in Duncan, Altus, Enid, Clinton, El Reno, and Chickasha. In addition to enhancing care for out-of-town patients, the network was also used for specialized training for staff members of the member hospitals.

Several milestones were reached in 1994. The Cancer Center of the Southwest was renamed the Troy and Dollie Smith Cancer Center, to recognize the Smith family's significant contributions that greatly enhanced BMC's services for cancer patients, survivors, and their families. Dr. Nazih Zuhdi performed the state's first double lung transplant and Dr. Bakr Nour performed Oklahoma's first pediatric liver transplant. With the support of Dr. Charles Bethea, BMC became the first hospital in Oklahoma to join the national Duke Database Project to track cardiac treatment outcomes.

In August, 1995, the Oklahoma Health System changed its name to INTEGRIS Health Inc. The stated mission was "To improve the health of the people and communities we serve." Baptist Medical Center officially became INTEGRIS Baptist Medical Center (IBMC). In addition to the name change, more "firsts" occurred at the medical center in 1995. The Hyperbaric Medicine and Wound Care Center opened within the Burn Center. A new 12-place hyperbaric chamber, the first of its kind in Oklahoma, promotes the healing of burns and wounds. Dr. Herbert L. Meites was named Medical Director.

The 10-bed Pediatric Intensive Care Unit opened to care for children with transplanted organs and other critical medical needs. Dr. Johnny R. Griggs was named Medical Director of the unit. Dr. Eliezer Katz led the team that performed the state's first live-donor liver transplant. Dr. Anthony Sebastian performed Oklahoma's first pancreas transplant.

When the Alfred P. Murrah Federal Building was destroyed by a bomb on April 19, 1995, many of the injured were brought to the emergency room at BMC. Later, members of the Dallas Cowboys professional football team visited the emergency room and congratulated workers. Cowboy players on the back row, left to right, are Larry Brown, Dixon Edwards, Darrin Smith, Mark Tuinei, and Daryl "Moose" Johnston.

IBMC's expanded community involvement programs were cited by the Voluntary Hospital Association (VHA), the nation's largest organization of not-for-profit hospitals, in 1996. The hospital received the VHA Leadership Award during the group's annual conference in Philadelphia, Pennsylvania. The award noted IBMC's free community clinic, free health screenings, flue vaccination programs, and the Calm Waters program for children.

Also in 1996, The PACER Fitness Center was honored by the Association of Hospital Health and Fitness as being the first hospital program in the nation created to provide rehabilitation and adult fitness. Don Schneider, one of the original administrators of the program, and Dr. Charles Bethea were recognized for building PACER into a world-class cardiopulmonary rehabilitation program.

In the mid-1990s, the hospital and health care industry again entered a significant period of transformation. With mergers and acquisitions, an increase in outpatient procedures, and managed care contracts, IBMC leaders pledged to preserve the medical center's position as the leading health care provider in Oklahoma City, but also promised to continue to make improvements to improve its market position in the coming decades. The consulting firm of Towers Perrin was engaged to assist the hospital in honoring the uniqueness of each organization, yet increase efficiency in patient services in a time when hospital revenues decreased because of managed care contracts and cuts in Medicare and Medicaid.

The Center for Mind, Body, and Spirit, a new education organization, was created in 1998. Dr. R. Murali Krishna, president of INTEGRIS Mental Health, unveiled the program that offered training and education programs for health care providers. William Carpenter, D. Min., director of pastoral care and outpatient counseling at IBMC, was named director of the Center that was committed to improve health by increasing awareness of the healing power of the connection between mind, body, and spirit.

A driving force behind the creation of the Center for Mind, Body, and Spirit was Oklahoma City attorney James L. Hall, Jr., who became involved in raising money for the establishment of the center after looking for answers about the healing power of the mind, body, and spirit during his own health crisis. Just before his death in September, 1998, the center was renamed the James L. Hall Jr. Center for Mind, Body, and Spirit.

More construction and renovations improved facilities at the medical center in 1997 and 1998. Floors in the East and West towers were renovated,

In 1996, Joe Melendez retired after working in the engineering department since the hospital opened in 1959. Left to right, Vice President of Human Resources Bob Quiring, Melendez, and Engineering Director David Hunter.

James L. Hall, Jr., received the 1998 Circles of Excellence Award from the INTEGRIS Baptist Medical Center Foundation. Left to right, William Carpenter, Dr. Murali Krishna, Hall, and Stan Hupfeld.

Drs. Cory Nagode and Louie Wall practiced medicine in the Baptist Family Clinic.

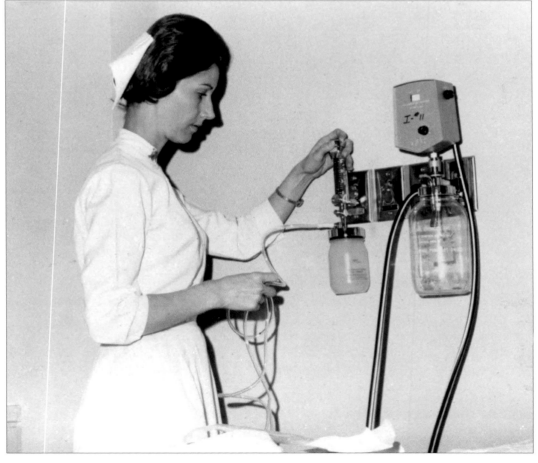

In the 1990s, Karen Miller was Director of Corporate Planning at Baptist Medical Center. She began as a nurse at the hospital in the early 1970s.

Buttons have been used through the years to promote new themes and promotional events at Baptist Medical Center.

Baptist Medical Center became part of INTEGRIS Health in 1995.

Facing Page: Stan Hupfeld, left, is congratulated in 1999 by Oklahoma City Mayor Ron Norick for launching a new hospital slogan, "We're Here for Life."

the post anesthesia recovery and ambulatory surgery units were expanded, ten new rehabilitation rooms were built in radiology, and the emergency department was doubled in size, including units for trauma/acute care and a satellite laboratory. The efforts won the approval of the Voluntary Hospital Association that awarded IBMC its national award for Clinical Effectiveness.

IBMC expanded its medical treatment options outside the campus on Northwest Highway. Dr. Bill Bondurant and Dr. Joe Jamison provided treatment at INTEGRIS Baptist Care Center North on North Pennsylvania in Oklahoma City and Dr. Donald Denmark, Dr. Mary Ann Bauman, and Dr. Hamed Albiek treated patients at the INTEGRIS Family Care Clinic in Edmond.

In April, 1999, the James L. Henry Endowment Fund for Indigent Patient Care was created at the annual Spring Gala hosted by the INTEGRIS Baptist Medical Center Foundation's Circle of Friends. The event raised $175,000 to fund the endowment in honor of the longtime administrator of the medical center. Karen Snyder and Jane Mathis Rutherford co-chaired the black-tie gala to raise money to benefit patients at IBMC who do not have the financial ability to cover all costs of needed medical care.

INTEGRIS Health

Meaning of INTEGRIS:

- **Integrated**—To bring together, to make whole, to provide seamless service, to assure quality.
- **Interrelated**—To effectively join; to partner with physicians, payors, programs, and services to insure efficient and effective healthcare delivery.
- **Informational**—To lead the region in medical information technology and community education.
- **Integral**—To be part of and vital to the provision of community health and medical services.
- **Integrity**—To possess core values, moral principles, honesty, and commitment to the Mission and Vision.

Strictly Confidential Copyright © -- GLENN MONIGLE AND ASSOCIATES

Courtesy Axiz Photography and Toby Nabors

CHAPTER 6

A Modern Medical Center

As a new century dawned in 2000, INTEGRIS Baptist Medical Center continued its quest for excellence—providing the best and newest medical treatment for residents of Oklahoma. For the fifth year in a row, IBMC was awarded the national Consumer Choice Award as one of the nation's top hospitals.

The INTEGRIS commitment to community service reached a new pinnacle with the founding of the state's first elementary charter school sponsored by a corporate entity. INTEGRIS Health President Stan Hupfeld was made aware that Western Village Elementary School near North Pennsylvania Avenue and Hefner Road in north Oklahoma City was about to be closed because of chronic low performance. The Oklahoma State Department of Education had designated the school as "high challenge." The inability to learn was further inhibited because of the rising juvenile crime rate in the area around the school.

Under Hupfeld's leadership, and with cooperation from Oklahoma City Public Schools, Western Village Academy was created on July 1, 2000. New employees were hired, facilities were renovated, and INTEGRIS employees began tutoring students in the low to middle income neighborhoods served by the school. INTEGRIS flooded the school with financial support and INTEGRIS volunteers began taking over the day-to-day operations of the school.

In the school's first decade, an exciting chapter in rescuing at-risk children has unfolded at Western Village. More than 300 INTEGRIS volunteers serve annually as mentors. Each student at the elementary school has an assigned tutor. The school's designation as "low performing" has been removed and students are reaching new levels of success. Enrollment has doubled and there is a long waiting list for prospective students.

INTEGRIS Health board chairman Luke Corbett, left, congratulates Stan Hupfeld after Western Village Academy is renamed in his honor in February, 2010. Hupfeld was honored by the Oklahoma State Department of Education for his vision for the charter school and was called "champion of children." *Courtesy Oklahoma Publishing Company.*

In 2006, Western Village received the Fit and Healthy Schools Program of Excellence Award-Best Practices Award, one of eight schools in the state so honored. In 2007, Western Village was the only Oklahoma charter school to make the list of 53 top schools across the nation as part of the National Charter School of the Year Program.

In 2010, the school earned national recognition by being named a Blue Ribbon Lighthouse School of Excellence award winner. Principal Peggy Brinson said, "With INTEGRIS Health as our business partner, supportive parents, and 300 mentors, we epitomize the adage, 'It takes a whole village to raise a child.'"

To honor the vision of the school's founder, Western Village Academy was renamed Stanley Hupfeld Academy at Western Village in February, 2010. A new sign was dedicated and INTEGRIS Health board chairman Luke Corbett cited improvements in the school, including its arts-integrated curriculum with specialists in visual art, music, dance, and literature.

In 2001, C. Bruce Lawrence became president and chief operating officer of IBMC. He previously was senior vice president and chief operating officer of Baptist Health in Montgomery, Alabama. Lawrence earned a masters degree in health administration from Trinity University in San Antonio, Texas.

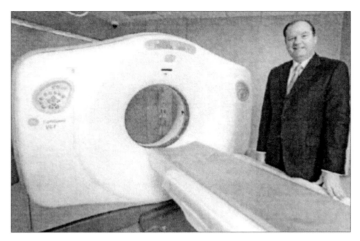

Bruce Lawrence, with the 64 slice CAT scanner in radiology at IBMC. Lawrence became president of IBMC in 2001 and president of INTEGRIS Health in 2010. *Courtesy Oklahoma Publishing Company.*

With the increase in employees and patients at IBMC, parking was a nightmare by 2002. To remedy the situation, a new, three-tier, 532,000-square-foot parking garage with 1,100 parking spaces was constructed. The $19 million project began in April, 2002, with the demolition of the 25-year-old, two-tier parking deck and garage on the east side of the medical center complex. The parking project was challenging because of heavy traffic in and out

It's art poster day at the Hupfeld Academy at Western Village, the INTEGRIS-sponsored charter elementary school.

of the complex. For awhile, employees had to be shuttled from distant parking lots to the hospital.

IBMC launched a Hispanic Initiative in 2003 to improve the quality of life in the growing Hispanic community in Oklahoma City. The Hispanic

Artist Greg Burns' interpretation of INTEGRIS Baptist Medical Center. *Courtesy Greg Burns.*

population in central Oklahoma doubled in the decade between 1995 and 2005 and is projected to be the dominant minority group by 2020. The goal of the INTEGRIS program is to use education, resources, and health-related services to provide medical treatment that sometimes is inhibited by language, cultural, or financial barriers.

IBMC became a tobacco-free zone in August, 2004, after administrators officially prohibited any smoking or other use of tobacco on the premises by employees, patients, or visitors. President Bruce Lawrence said, "We needed to take a stand. It's the right thing to do."

Stan Hupfeld introduces Oklahoma Fit Kids Coalition, a program to improve the health of Oklahoma's children.

Honorees at the 2005 Circle of Excellence event. Left to right, Larry Nichols, Polly Nichols, V. Burns Hargis, Suzie Hupfeld, and Stan Hupfeld.

Sharon Williams retired as a registered nurse at IBMC in 2008, 46 years after she arrived on campus as a student in the Baptist Memorial Hospital School of Nursing in 1962. When she began, the hospital had no intensive care unit, so cardiac patients were sent directly from the emergency room to the floor. At the time of her retirement, Williams was the longest-tenured nurse at IBMC.

Left to right, nurses Cheryl Smith, Kay Shields Ragan, and Brad Barnett took part in the 2007 Sabbatical Program, which provides paid leave for registered nurses to pursue projects that improve patient care or organizational performance.

After Hurricane Katrina devastated the Gulf Coast in 2005, thousands of residents were evacuated to Camp Gruber near Muskogee, Oklahoma. To render aid to the hurricane victims, more than 50 nurses volunteered their time at Camp Gruber or in Louisiana at the heart of the disaster. Debbie Risinger, a cardiovascular case management nurse at IBMC, volunteered at Camp Gruber. She said, "It was heart wrenching when we had to go find someone in the barracks where the evacuees were staying. They had all their stuff around their bunk and I realized that it was their whole world for now."

Going to Louisiana to assist hurricane victims was a life changing experience for nurse Eva Melrose of 9 East at IBMC. "It was the hardest experience of my life, both physically and mentally, yet one of the most rewarding. I became a better person and nurse because of what I saw and learned."

Visits to the emergency room increased more than 35 percent in the first six years of the new century, necessitating a $21 million expansion that allowed 27 percent more urgent care patients to be treated each year. An emergency room expansion just seven years before had proved inadequate. In the late 1990s, 37,000 patients were treated in the emergency room each year. By 2006, the number jumped to more than 55,000. Kevin Graves, vice

president of operations, suggested the increase was due to problems with accessibility of medical care and a growing number of patients with no insurance.

The expansion added the Naifeh Families Chest Pain Center, a separate emergency room area for patients to get immediate treatment to prevent permanent heart damage. In addition, a new ambulance canopy accommodated up to four ambulances and can be converted into a mass decontamination area in case of public emergencies involving chemicals or highly contagious diseases. The new emergency room also featured a centrally located nurses station that connected to a 12,000-square-foot outpatient radiology department that was completed in 2006. For the first time, patients were able to access radiology services, including diagnostic radiology, CT scan, and ultrasound without leaving the main floor of the hospital.

In November, 2006, Chris Hammes was named president of IBMC. Hammes, the former administrator of INTEGRIS Southwest Medical Center, replaced Bruce Lawrence who assumed the role of chief operating officer of INTEGRIS Health Inc. Lawrence had been president of both Baptist and Southwest medical centers before the corporate restructuring split the president's job at the two hospitals.

In 2007, the Baptist Heritage Room opened on the first floor of the main hospital to tell the history of INTEGRIS Baptist Medical Center. A multimedia approach was created by a team led by Judy Hoisington, Sally Ritcheson Burks, and Ann Shaff directing content. Bill Shawn provided audio-video resources, John Mesa and Ann Ozan Willis were responsible for conceptual design, and David Foss was the construction manager.

Santa Claus visiting a child in 2008 in the pediatric unit. *Courtesy Oklahoma Publishing Company.*

In 2007, IBMC received one of the highest levels of recognition a medical center can earn by being given the Magnet designation for excellence in nursing services by the American Nurses Credentialing Center. Linda Merkey, IBMC chief nursing officer said, "It simply recognizes the excellent work our nurses and physicians do each day and reflects the commitment of our entire staff to serve as a team, providing the highest quality care possible for the people of our community."

IBMC became only the 250th medical center nationwide to receive the Magnet designation, nursing's highest honor. Only two percent of hospitals in the nation have been so recognized. The IBMC effort to gain Magnet designation was coordinated by Cheryl Smith, project director, assisted by nurses Tara Rose, April Merrill, Terri Adams-Beck, Kenna Wilson, Lisa Rother, and Susie Jones.

The year 2007 was exceptional for the hospital receiving awards. IBMC ranked in the top five hospitals in the nation for the American Hospital Association's McKesson Quest for Quality Award. Voluntary Hospitals of America presented three awards to IBMC for improved performance in hand hygiene, outstanding treatment for heart problems, and a reduction in surgical infection and pneumonia.

Patients line up for free medical care at the Baptist Community Clinic at Olivet Baptist Church. The clinic has been staffed by volunteers three times a month since it opened in 1993. Each year, more than 3,000 patients are seen and nearly 16,000 prescriptions filled.

BAPTIST "FIRSTS" IN THE NEW CENTURY

2000
- Western Village Elementary becomes an INTEGRIS Health Charter School

2003
- East parking garage opens

2004
- Campus becomes tobacco free

2006
- For five years of improvement in clinical and management outcomes, hospital receives Solucient Top 100 Hospital Performance Improvement Leader's Award
- First bloodless surgery performed on a live liver transplant patient

2007
- Nursing staff awarded Magnet Designation by the American Nurses Credentialing Center for outstanding service
- Construction begins on state's first proton therapy cancer treatment center

2008
- First implantation in Oklahoma of the Tandem-Heart, the latest in heart pump Technology
- Two new Centers of Excellence recognized—M.J. and S. Elizabeth Schwartz Sleep Disorders Center and James R. Daniel Cerebrovascular & Stroke Center

2009
- First implantation in Oklahoma of the Impella 2.5 Cardiac Assist Device, the world's smallest heart pump
- On Valentine's Day weekend, Nazih Zuhdi Transplantation Institute participates in world's first six-way kidney transplant

2010
- Western Village Academy is renamed Stanley Hupfeld Academy at Western Village
- Troy Golden becomes second Total Artificial Heart patient in nation to leave the hospital using a portable driver to power his heart.

In 2008, more specialized programs were accredited by national agencies, The Advanced Cardiac Care Program, under the direction of Dr. Doug Horstmanshof, is one of only 15 centers in the nation to be certified. The Surgical Weight Loss Program, developed by Dr. Russell Gornichec and today under the guidance of Dr. Hamilton Le, offers the only dually accredited bariatric program in the state. The Hyperglycemia Program, part of the advanced diabetes treatment program directed by Dr. John S. Muchmore, was the first such program in the nation to be accredited.

Emergency medical transport was improved in 2009 when INTEGRIS teamed with EagleMed that began housing a helicopter just west of the hospital. A medically-equipped fixed-wing aircraft was also available at Sundance Airport to be used when inclement weather prohibited helicopter flight and for organ procurement.

IBMC leadership recognizes the important of informing the public about better health and safety practices. Hugga T. Bear, the hospital's mascot,

INTEGRIS attorney John Vera completes a deposition of a witness.

In 2010, the IBMC Volunteer Auxiliary celebrated its 50th anniversary. At the celebration, left to right, are Jay Henry, Margaret Henry, Ed Koop, Ursula Lewis, Daisy McNeill, and Bill Hinkle. *Courtesy Oklahoma Publishing Company.*

teaches children the Stop, Drop and Roll procedure at day care centers and elementary schools. The Move for Life program helps target the problem of childhood obesity by educating children about nutrition and the importance of physical activity.

Special programs for Hispanics and African American men and women are regularly scheduled. The INTEGRIS Men's Health University, created in 2004, offers a series of events designed to educate men and their families of the importance of men taking charge of their own health. The Women's Health Forum is one of Oklahoma City's most popular annual events with nationally-known speakers presenting information on women's health needs. Mobile Meals provides meals five days a week to people unable to leave their residence.

Asthma Education Clinics are made fun to take the message about the condition to area schools. Camp Funnybone is a five-day camp each year to teach children, ages six to 14, positive lessons about themselves. Children from all social and economic circumstances learn clowning skills to build self confidence and self worth. The Basic Educational Empowerment Program (BEEP), founded in 1995, continues to help youth who are "at risk" of criminal activity obtain a marketable skill through education. The program was originally founded to assist gang members to become productive citizens.

The hospital celebrated its 50th anniversary in 2009. Judy Hoisington, Sally Ritcheson Burks, and John Mesa produced a 50th anniversary book that applauded the many "firsts" of the hospital. Not wanting to rest on laurels of the past, President Chris Hammes said, "We hope to have many more patient firsts in the future for the benefit of the community and state."

Just another night of entertainment from the boys at IBMC. Left to right, Karl Weinmeister, Stan Hupfeld, and Bruce Lawrence.

A Christmas program at Children's Place.

In June, 2009, a major leadership change was announced. Effective at the end of the year, Stan Hupfeld resigned as president and CEO of INTEGRIS Health to become chairman of the INTEGRIS Family of Foundations. Hupfeld was succeeded at INTEGRIS Health by Bruce Lawrence. In 2013, INTEGRIS Health was the state's largest not-for-profit health care provider with a statewide system of 13 hospitals and more than 9,000 employees. Nearly two million Oklahomans receive health care from INTEGRIS each year.

INTEGRIS' community outreach went global in 2009. Zora Brown, Deborah Burroughs, and Dr. Johnny Griggs coordinated a medical mission trip to Nigeria. Much of the cost of the trip was underwritten by the INTEGRIS Family of Foundations. More than 500 patients were provided examinations, medicines, medical procedures, and education. Supplies and teaching materials were left at clinics visited in Nigeria. A team of 12 doctors and nurses joined two dozen support personnel on the trip. Dr. Griggs wrote in his journal about the treatment of a child by Dr. Okey Nwokolo:

> Dr. Nwokolo saved the life of the second child he saw on our first day. The two-year-old would have easily been in my Pediatric Intensive Care Unit in Oklahoma City. We gave this child about 5 times as much fluid as we would in a hospital setting...because we knew this would be his only opportunity to get fluids in this barren environment. Several hours later, he was bounding on his happy father's lap!

Tim Johnsen, a native of St. Louis, Missouri, became president of IBMC in January, 2013. He replaced Chris Hammes who was promoted to executive vice president and chief operating officer of INTEGRIS' network of hospital operations.

When visionaries began dreaming of a Baptist hospital in Oklahoma City, they recognized that spiritual support and a spirit of volunteerism, both in the hospital and the community, would need to be present at a high level if the hospital became a lighthouse of medical care for Oklahomans. In that tradition, the Department of Pastoral Care provides spiritual support for patients, families, and hospital staff. Chaplains make daily rounds and are always available. Ecumenical worship services are held each Sunday in the R.C. Howard, Jr. Chapel, named for a longtime supporter and Governing Board member.

The Volunteer Auxiliary provides more than 400 active and associate members with opportunities to serve in 35 areas around the IBMC campus. Many types of service for patients are performed by volunteers, including in the Gift Gallery, Information Desk, Flower Room, Patient Mail Service, Visitor Guest Bed Hospitality Service, and the Third Age Life Center.

Many people volunteer as a result of a personal experience as a patient or family member. In 2010, the Volunteer Auxiliary donated $1 million to the INTEGRIS Hospice House, a 12-bed facility to provide a home-like atmosphere where patients receive care.

Good medical care sometimes produces a bond between the hospital and patient. When Corrine Thompson, a Colorado artist, died in 2011, she left more than $500,000 to IBMC for an event that occurred 35 years before. In 1976, Thompson was visiting friends in Oklahoma City when she suffered a massive heart attack. She was rushed to IBMC where surgeons saved her life with open-heart surgery. She never forgot and, at the end of her life, she remembered the excellent and life-saving treatment she received.

IBMC continues to excel into its second half-century of service. In July, 2012, *U.S. News & World Report* ranked the hospital No. 1 in Oklahoma City in a review of several areas of medical service.

If the hospital's first Chief of Staff, Dr. Henry G. Bennett, Jr., community giants such as Robert S. Kerr, Stanley Draper, and Raymond Young, and Baptist leaders Dr. T.B. Lackey and Dr. Joe Ingram were alive today, no doubt they would drive by the sprawling complex that occupies the hill that once lay barren, and say, "Job Well Done!"

Dr. Sami Dahr, right, and surgical assistant Anthony Williams perform scleral buckling surgery to repair a detached retina in a 2010 procedure at IBMC.

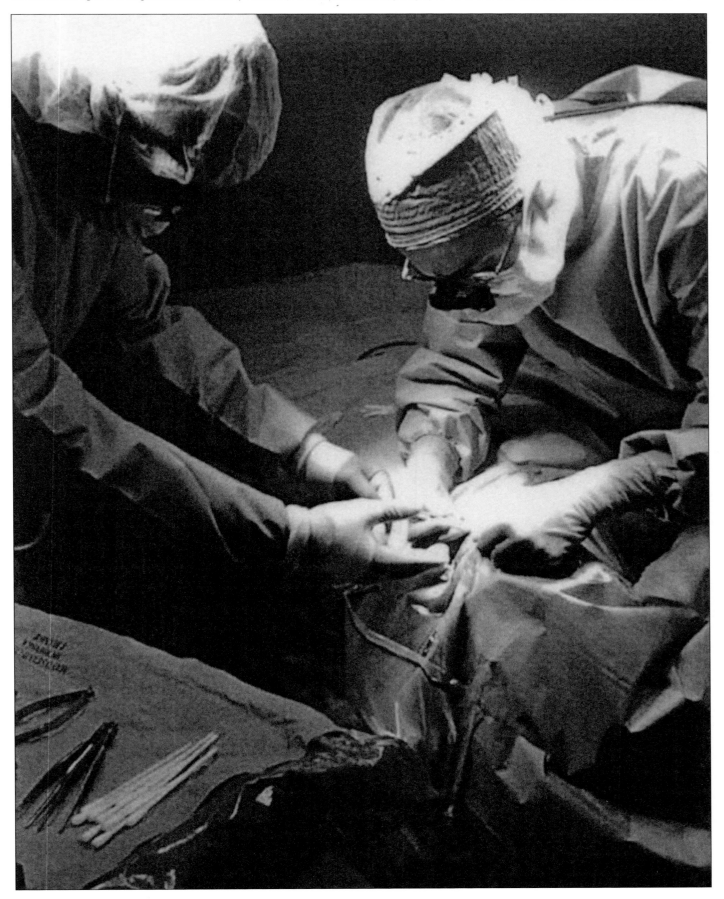

INTEGRIS

INTEGRIS	Nazih Zuhdi
Heart Hospital	**Transplant Institute**

Hough	Paul Silverstein
Ear Institute	**Burn Center**

Jim Thorpe	James R. Daniel
Rehabilitation Hospital	**Cerebrovascular & Stroke Center**

EXIT ONLY   EMPLOYEE PARKING

Courtesy Axiz Photography and Toby Nabors

CENTERS OF EXCELLENCE

Transplant Institute

Paul Silverstein
Burn Center

James R. Daniel
Cerebrovascular

Courtesy Axiz Photography and Toby Nabors

CHAPTER 7

Paul Silverstein Burn Center

In 1975, Dr. Paul Silverstein was completing his residency in plastic surgery at Emory University in Atlanta, Georgia. A native of Boston, Silverstein was committed to developing new treatment techniques in plastic and reconstructive surgery, especially for burn patients. He had served as a Major in the U.S. Army Medical Corps at Fort Sam Houston, Texas, where he treated soldiers who had been burned and injured in the Vietnam War.

Dr. Paul Silverstein pioneered the Burn Center at Baptist Medical Center.

In Oklahoma, Baptist Hospital administrator Jay Henry and Dr. Ed Dalton were interested in establishing a center to treat burn patients. The only hospital space in Oklahoma committed to burn patients was at Hillcrest Hospital in Tulsa. Plastic surgeons in Oklahoma City and as far away as the Texas Panhandle saw the need for a Burn Center in Oklahoma City.

Dr. Dalton was familiar with Dr. Silverstein's work. After a few telephone calls, Dr. Silverstein agreed to join Dalton in his plastic surgery practice in Oklahoma City. Unfortunately, there was competition for a Burn Center. The University of Oklahoma Health Sciences Center also applied to the State Health Planning Agency for approval of a special facility for burn patients. There was a reluctance to approve either application because of the high cost of operation and the assumption that many patients would be treated in such a center on a "no-pay" basis.

Henry, Dalton, and Silverstein were persistent. Eugene T. White, the former development director at the Oklahoma Medical Research Foundation, was retained by BMC to raise money to fund a Burn Center. Henry and White traveled the state, making presentations to potential donors. The Kerr Foundation agreed to contribute $500,000 if a matching amount could be raised. Baptist leaders targeted companies whose workers were subject to high risks for burns. Soon, commitments were received to make the Burn Center possible.

The political squabble caused by the competition between BMC and the OU Health Sciences Center was resolved in favor of BMC. Lloyd Rader, the director of the Oklahoma Department of Human Services, chaired a special committee that ultimately decided that the proper place for a burn center was Baptist Medical Center. The State Health Planning Agency approved the application in the summer of 1975.

On November 24, 1975, the Baptist Burn Center opened with eight acute care and three convalescent care beds on the third floor of the West Tower. Within weeks, it was obvious to Dr. Silverstein and his staff that more space was needed. Additional money was raised to expand the Burn Center to encompass the entire third floor. By May, 1976, the Center had 11 acute care beds and 21 private and semi-private rooms in the south wing that evolved into a progressive care area for convalescent burn patients.

In its first eight months of operation, the Burn Center treated 69 patients from electrical and chemical burns and explosions. They ranged in age from

two months to 77 years. Amazingly, the cost per patient per day was only $325, including the hospital absorbing the entire cost of $112,000 for a patient who had no ability to pay. From the beginning, the Burn Center's policy was to admit any patient who needed care, regardless of ability to pay.

Dr. Silverstein's goal was to "rehabilitate a patient, not just save a life." He said, "If a patient leaves here a whole person and productive member of society, then we have accomplished our goal."

Often, treatment of horribly burned patients received wide media attention. An example is 1980 was the treatment that saved the life of truck driver Ray McVey. When Ray arrived at the Burn Center, he was placed in the three-bed intensive care area. Doctors and nurses immediately started intravenous therapy to reestablish the patient's fluid levels and prevent him from going into shock. IV therapy also kept the unconscious McVey alive as treatment of the severe burns and other injuries took place.

McVey's case was followed by the media. With

A ribbon-cutting ceremony opened the Baptist Burn Center on November 23, 1975. Left to right, Burn Center director Dr. Paul Silverstein, Governing Board chairman Ken Bonds, burn expert and president of the American Burn Association Colonel Basil Pruitt, Jr., and Brenda Van Zandt, director of nursing services in the West Tower.

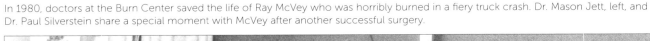

In 1980, doctors at the Burn Center saved the life of Ray McVey who was horribly burned in a fiery truck crash. Dr. Mason Jett, left, and Dr. Paul Silverstein share a special moment with McVey after another successful surgery.

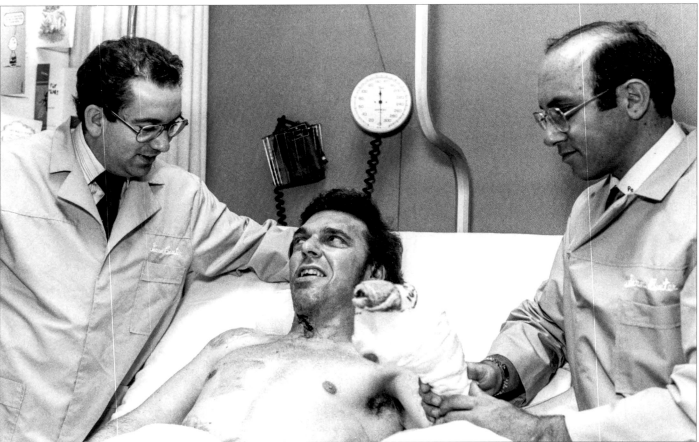

an extraordinary will to live, McVey underwent extensive surgeries and therapy. It was a major event when he walked for the first time. His wife, Mary, remembered, "The whole room was full. It happened on a shift change when a new crew was coming on. Nurses donned visitors' gowns and rushed to his room. Some of them cried because they were so proud of Ray."

The treatment of McVey emphasized the uniqueness of staff at the Burn Center. Nurse Supervisor Pat Norvell explained:

This type of nursing requires a special kind of maturity. It requires someone who can handle delayed gratification. We're geared in nursing school to do something for the patient and they thank us. Here, we may not be thanked for several weeks, but in the meantime, we still continue to give the same level of care.

Exceptional nurses were sought to train to meet the specific needs of burn patients. Soon, the

key members of the Burn Center were recognized nationally for their work.

In 1989, the Burn Center expanded to include hyperbaric oxygen (HBO) therapy. An HBO chamber allowed a patient to breath pure oxygen while the pressure was increased to six times normal atmospheric pressure. The painless procedure was equivalent to a patient being 30 feet underwater. The concentration of oxygen improved healing of tissue, not only for burn victims but also speeded the recovery of deteriorated bone tissue in a woman with cancer of the jaw and saved a man from brain injury or possible death from carbon monoxide poisoning. Dr. John Huff, pulmonologist, and Dr. William E. Hood, Jr., obstetrician-gynecologist, were the first directors of the HBO therapy.

By 2000, the Burn Center at BMC expanded to not only provide top-level care to burn victims, but also performed clinical research to stay at the leading edge of new techniques. Dr. Silverstein and Dr. Meites led educational seminars for physicians

A burn patient receives the latest innovative treatment in 1984.

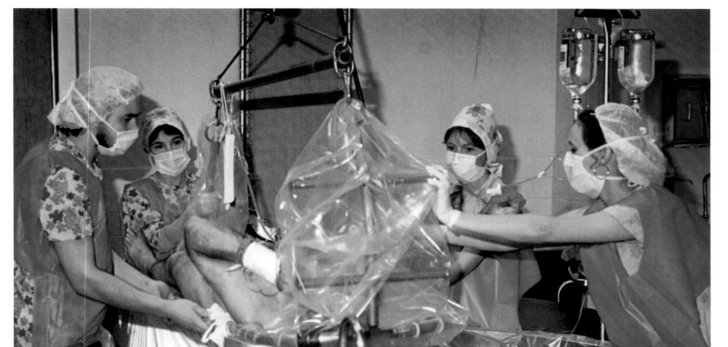

Nursing skills, sophisticated equipment, innovative techniques, and talented burn care specialist come together in the Burn Center in the 1980s.

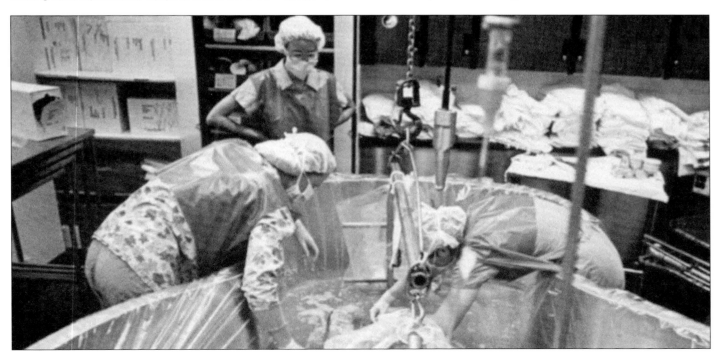

Dr. Paul Silverstein demonstrates the Burn Center's new hyperbaric oxygen chamber in 1989. Similar to an iron lung, the chamber increased the oxygen content of a patient's blood, improving their supply of life-giving oxygen to bodily tissue. The unit was purchased by a gift from the Samuel Roberts Noble Foundation.

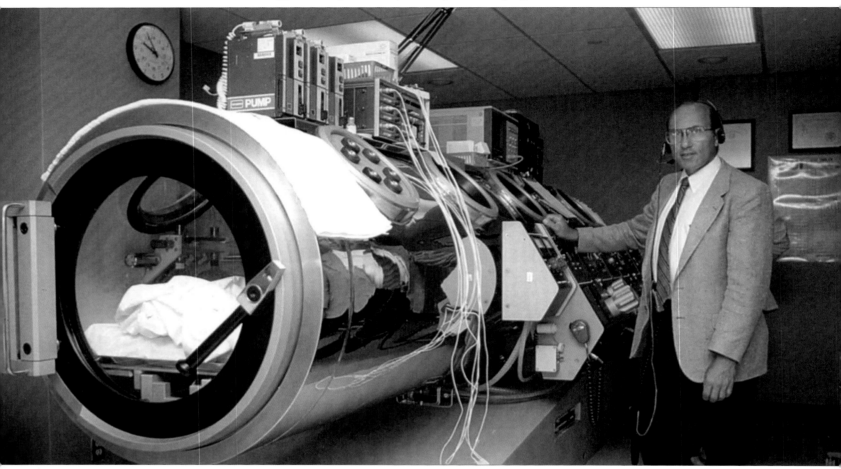

and other medical professionals in burn care. In addition, programs on burn prevention and fire safety at home and on the job were presented to fire departments, ambulance workers, and civic, church, and industrial groups.

In 1992, Dr. Silverstein and his Burn Center staff were honored by the American Burn Association for promoting flame-retardant children's sleepwear to prevent burn injuries. They were also cited for advocating fire-safe cigarettes.

Dr. Silverstein served as clinical professor of plastic surgery at the University of Oklahoma College of Medicine and lectured nationally and internationally to medical service providers. He led efforts in 1995 for the purchase of a 12-place hyperbaric chamber and the establishment of a separate hyperbaric

A major advance in treatment of burn victims came with the installation of a 12-person hyperbaric chamber in 1995.

Dr. Paul Silverstein, left, and longtime Burn Center Supervisor Dorothy Richardson.

medicine and wound care center. In 2003, Silverstein receive the Harvey Stuart Allen Distinguished Service Award, the highest national honor for a specialist in burn treatment.

The popularity of the Burn Center as a top-level care facility required two major renovations since its founding. In the early 1990s, space was renovated to include much need physical and occupational therapy and hydrotherapy cubicles. The rise in outpatient treatment necessitated the building of more space.

For saving the lives of two firemen burned in a house fire, the Baptist Burn Center was honored in 1989. Left to right, Oklahoma City Deputy Fire Chief Jon Hansen, Dr. Paul Silverstein, Burn Center medical director Gail Maxwell, and Fire Chief Tom Smith.

A crane had to lift the huge hyperbaric chamber into place prior to completion of exterior walls and a roof over the facility.

After initial stabilization of a patient, physicians used the most advanced techniques for skin grafting and replacement. One of the procedures is called Integra, an advanced wound-care device made up of an inner layer of cow collagen and shark cartilage and an outer layer of silicone to protect the burned area from infection. The technique lessens the risk of scarring by supporting regrowth of the deeper layers of the skin.

In its first 37 years of operation, the Paul Silverstein Burn Center treated more than 5,000 patients in a six-state area. Another 10,000 patients received care on an outpatient basis. The Burn Center is one of the largest and most technologically advanced facilities of its kind in the United States. In December, 2012, Dr. Christopher Lentz became the medical director of the Burn Center.

In 2000, the doctors of the Paul Silverstein Burn Center were, left to right, Dr. Olaselinde Sawyerr, Dr. Silverstein, Dr. Herbert Meites, and Dr. Mason Jett.

INTEGRIS

INTEGRIS
Heart Hospital

Hough
Ear Institute

Courtesy Axiz Photography and Toby Nabors

CHAPTER 8

INTEGRIS Heart Hospital

Baptist Medical Center provided cardiology treatment for patients from the time the hospital opened in 1959. A Department of Cardiology was established at the hospital in the early 1960s. Dr. Nazih Zuhdi's first open-heart surgery in 1963 paved the way for the hospital to become a leader in cardiovascular surgery and innovation, as well as advances in other fields of medicine. The Cardiac Surgery unit was also established that same year.

The program's cutting edge achievements gave it distinction as the first of what later became Centers of Excellence at the hospital. Radioisotope therapy and cardiac catheterization procedures were introduced by Drs. Galen P. Robbins and John J. Donnell in the mid-1960s.

In 1983, the Oklahoma Heart Center, with Dr. Zuhdi as chairman, was established at BMC. The Center's stated goals were:

> To promote a superior environment in Oklahoma for the care of patients with cardiovascular disease.

> To promote education and training for health professionals in the field of cardiovascular disease.

> To serve as a resource for the stimulation and facilitation of clinical and basic research.

> To initiate and continue educational programs for Oklahomans aimed at maintaining a health state and prevention of heart disease.

In the 1990s, there was a desire among heart doctors to move treatment of heart disease at IBMC to a new level. In 2000, a group of cardiologists and the hospital administration developed a collaborative program to create a world-class heart program. The concept allowed highly-trained teams to focus on delivering excellent health care treatment, with other medical specialties only a few seconds away should the care be necessary for the patient. The heart hospital was really a hospital within a hospital.

INTEGRIS Heart Hospital (IHH) is the largest and most comprehensive cardiac program in Oklahoma. Services range from heart scans, cardiac catheterization, and open heart surgery, to heart transplantation. IHH has more than 170 beds spread across two floors of the medical center. Its model is unique. Unlike other facilities that provide a financial incentive to their owners to increase profits, the IHH aims to provide the highest level of care possible. For that purpose, it was named one of the Top 100 Heart Hospitals in the nation in 1999 by HCIA, Inc.

IHH is proud to claim the state's first heart transplant program, the first hospital-based cardiac rehabilitation program, the first 3-D imaging cardiac catheterization laboratory, the first and only clear heart scan picture using EBCT technology, the first 320 Slice CT imaging technology, the first hospital-based fitness center, PACER, and headline-making research studies and primary research on the first drug-eluting stent produced and used in the United States. IHH was one of only 12 sites worldwide to participate in all three research trials associated with the technology.

When the IHH was established, leaders established outreach clinics in outlying communities. The purpose was for INTEGRIS Baptist physicians to see heart patients in their own cities and towns. Beginning with a few clinics, the program was expanded to 26 in 2011.

In 2003, Dr. John Chaffin and Dr. Craig Elkins implanted a portable left-ventricular assist device, or portable heart pump, in a patient. It was the first procedure of its kind in Oklahoma and was "an astounding and lifesaving merger between man and machine." In the same year, IHH was the first facility to implant the groundbreaking drug-eluting stent in two patients on the same day, after approval of the device by the Food and Drug Administration.

In 2005, Franklin and Robert Naifeh and their families contributed $300,000 to create the Naifeh Families Chest Pain Center. The Center made it possible to treat patients with chest pain immediately when they arrive at the emergency room. Personnel work with ambulance attendants to administer lifesaving help within seconds of arriving at the hospital. Ambulance crews can send EKG's and other vital data to the hospital while still en route. Naifeh Center staff can begin preparing for the patient's arrival as they communicate with paramedics. It is a head start that can sometimes be the difference between life and death. The Naifeh Center has been accredited by the National Society of Chest Pain Centers, the first designation in Oklahoma, and only the sixth facility in the nation to receive such recognition. Bruce Lawrence, executive vice president and COO of INTEGRIS Health, said, "The fact that we were the first in the state to reach this next level of care is another example of Baptist's commitment to the community."

Through the generosity of the Samuel Roberts Noble Foundation, the bi-plane angiography suite was constructed and opened at the Oklahoma Heart Center in 1985. The bi-plane Angioskop is shown to visitors by Dr. Ronald H. White.

Also in 2005, IBMC launched a gender-specific program designed to address women's heart health. The Heart Essentials program, the first of its kind in Oklahoma, helps women assess their heart care needs which can be different from men's. Terrie Gibson, IHH cardiologist and Heart Essentials co-director, said, "Since women are less likely to survive a heart attack than men, Heart Essentials is intended to empower women to know their heart risks before the disease strikes them."

State-of-the art techniques continue to provide unprecedented cardiac care at IHH. The heart pump has given new hope for heart patients. Dr.

James Long, who became director of the Oklahoma Advanced Heart Failure team in 2008, joined Dr. Craig Elkins and Dr. Doug Horstmanshof in implanting a self-contained, battery-powered heart pump into Augustus "Gus" Harbert of Tulsa in March, 2008. Dr. Long called the heart pump, "a great milestone for the field of mechanical circulatory-support therapy and for many heart-failure patients." He said the pump, as the newest weapon against heart disease, will not only extend life, but will improve its quality. The device is planted alongside a patient's heart and takes over the pumping of the weakened heart's left ventricle. IHH was one of only 44 American medical

The PACER Fitness Center has been a part of the cardiology treatment program at BMC since its inception. Member Jack Miller lost substantial weight on the OPTIFAST program in the late 1980s, combining the liquid diet plus behavior modification and exercise.

centers to participate in clinical trials of the implantable HeartMate pump.

Dr. Long was attracted to IBMC for several reasons. He said, "I was drawn here by desperate needs and a group of experts committed to excellence. Building on a great heritage, I intend for Oklahomans to have access to the very best therapies available anywhere in the world."

IHH was recognized in 2009 with the Gold Performance Achievement Award, one of only 121 hospitals in the nation to receive the award from the American College of Cardiology Foundation. For several years, IHH has been designated as the Top Cardiac Provider in Oklahoma by HealthGrades, Inc.

The Heart Failure Institute within the heart hospital provides patients a team of 10-15 specialists including cardiologists, cardiac surgeons, clinical registered nurses, dieticians, pharmacists, rehabilitation nurses, and social workers. Also, IHH offers heart valve repair and replacement, electrophysiology, the study of the heart's electrical system, and participation in the Mended Hearts support group. The group's purpose is to provide educational and emotional support for heart patients, families, and caregivers.

In 2010, IHH doctors became the first in the nation to implant a new type of heart pump that

Dr. Charles F. Bethea was chairman of the Division of Cardiology at BMC in 1987, and was largely responsible for the development of the PACER Fitness Center.

flows continuously and is more durable that previous models. The Levacor ventricular assist device, made by World Heart Corporation, was implanted in two Oklahoma patients by Dr. Craig Elkins as part of clinical testing of the device. The patients, a 59-year-old woman and a 36-year-old man, suffered from severe cardiomyopathy, or a weakened heart muscle.

In September, 2010, IHH physicians made news again. Troy Golden, a 45-year-old Geary, Oklahoma, pastor became the first patient in the region to have his heart replaced with the SynCardia Total Artificial Heart. A month later, Golden was only the second Total Artificial Heart patient in the country to leave the hospital using a portable driver to power the heart while waiting on a transplant. The new era in heart treatment excited Dr. James Long. He said, "This technology could open up a whole new world for our patients by allowing them to wait for a heart surrounded by the people they love in the comfortable and familiar setting of their own home."

In 2011, IHH was the first hospital in the state to use the advanced Aquilion ONE CT scanning system. Toshiba developed the system to replace several tests with a single exam, allowing physicians to treat at-risk patients immediately.

In 2011, INTEGRIS Heart Hospital provided cardiology services at 26 outreach clinics.

Gus Harbert holds his two-year-old son, Cameron, during a news conference following his heart pump implantation at IBMC in March, 2008. *Courtesy Oklahoma Publishing Company.*

Paul Silverstein
Burn Center

ospital

James R. Daniel
**Cerebrovascular
& Stroke Center**

Courtesy Axiz Photography and Toby Nabors

CHAPTER 9

James R. Daniel Cerebrovascular & Stroke Center

Baptist Medical Center provided cardiology treatment for patients from the time the hospital opened in 1959. A Department of Cardiology was established at the hospital in the early 1960s. Dr. Nazih Zuhdi's first open-heart surgery in 1963 paved the way for the hospital's entrance into major heart care, as well as advances in other fields of medicine. The Cardiac Surgery unit was also established that same year.

James R. "Jim" Daniel, president of Friendly National Bank, joined the Baptist Medical Center Governing Board in 1973. His 2007 endowment helped create a modern stroke center.

Sometimes, good things result from bad situations. Oklahoma City banker James R. "Jim" Daniel lost both parents to strokes. His father, Reverend John T. Daniel, was one of the first volunteer chaplains at BMC and was a fundraiser for the Baptist Golden Age Retirement Homes. The family experience with the devastation caused by strokes made Jim Daniel critically aware of the need for research for better ways to treat stroke victims.

In 2007, Daniel donated $1 million to INTEGRIS to help establish a permanent endowment to support stroke centers at INTEGRIS Baptist Medical Center and INTEGRIS Southwest Medical Center. Daniel was a longtime supporter of Baptist. He joined the Governing Board of the hospital in 1973, eventually serving as its chairman. When Baptist Medical Center became part of INTEGRIS Health in 1995, he became a member of the INTEGRIS board and served as chairman in 2001 and 2002. In 2001, Daniel received the Award of Excellence in recognition of his lifelong commitment to the hospital.

The James R. Daniel Cerebrovascular & Stroke Center at BMC is nationally accredited and offers comprehensive stroke care, from prevention and education to treatment and rehabilitation of patients.

Recognizing that persons experiencing stroke symptoms must be treated quickly, the INTEGRIS TeleStroke Network was created as a two-way interactive video conferencing system between BMC and regional hospitals. Often, smaller hospitals do not have sufficient staff and equipment to treat stroke patients rapidly and effectively. The network allows health care professionals and hospitals in Enid, Yukon, Blackwell, Madill, Duncan, Idabel, and Clinton to video conference with a stroke neurologist in Oklahoma City to make the urgent decision whether to administer the t-PA clot-busting medication to a patient.

In 2008, the Stroke Center earned the Gold Seal of Approval from The Joint Commission for Primary Stroke Centers. Dr. Lawrence Davis, neurologist and director of the Stroke Center, led the medical and administrative team that asked for the stringent national review to make certain that the Stroke Center at IBMC followed national standards and guidelines that significantly improve outcomes for stroke patients.

In 2010, the American Heart Association and the American Stroke Association recognized IBMC for its success in using the Get With the Guidelines program to improve quality of care for heart disease and patients who suffer strokes.

TEGRIS

Nazih Zuhdi
Transplant Institute

Paul Silverstein
Burn Center

Courtesy Axiz Photography and Toby Nabors

CHAPTER 10

Nazih Zuhdi
Transplant Institute

The transplant institute at Baptist Medical
Center is named for Dr. Nazih Zuhdi,
its founder, and one of the five scientists—
heart surgeons— who are acclaimed
as pioneers, the "originals" of the surgical
treatment of the heart and all that followed.

Born in Beirut, Lebanon, Dr. Nazih Zuhdi graduated in 1950 with his Doctor of Medicine Degree from the American University of Beirut before immigrating to the United States. With a surgical internship in 1951 at New York-Presbyterian, Columbia University Medical Center he had the opportunity to work with Dr. Arthur Voorhees, who was developing synthetic vascular grafts. From 1952 to 1956 he continued his medical training under the tutelage of Dr. Clarence Dennis at the State University of New York–Downstate Medical Center in Brooklyn, including work in Dennis' laboratories dealing with heart-lung machines and total-body perfusions. Dennis penned Zuhdi as a "co-worker." In the early days of open-heart surgery at the University of Minnesota, it was during 1956 when Zuhdi learned the corrective procedures of heart defects from Dr. C. Walton Lillehei and was assigned studies that he performed on the DeWall-Lillehei pump oxygenator. Lillehei referred to Zuhdi as a "master surgeon."

It was a special time in medical history. In 1953, Dr. John Gibbon performed the first successful open-heart surgery using his heart-lung machine at the Jefferson Medical College in Philadelphia, Pennsylvania.

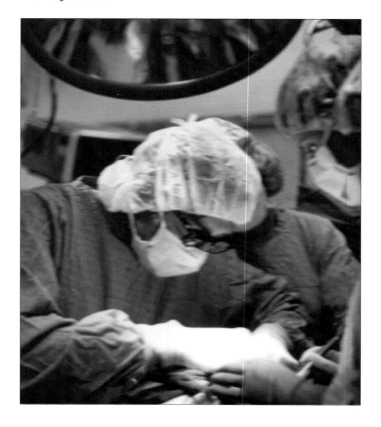

During the four-hour operation, Chief Surgeon Dr. Nazih Zuhdi replaced Nancy Rogers' heart with the heart of a 14-year-old girl who had been killed in an automobile accident.

Dr. Nazih Zuhdi addresses reporters after performing the first heart transplant in Oklahoma at Baptist Medical Center in 1985. Left to right, chief surgeon Dr. Zuhdi, medical student and observer Dr. John Zweicker, Mercy Hospital's Dr. Kenneth Potts, Rogers' referring cardiologist, and second assistant Dr. David Vanhooser. Not shown were Mercy's Dr. Raoul Chanes, Rogers' oncologist and referring physician, and St. Anthony's Dr. Ted Violett who performed some of Rogers' lab work, and first assistant Dr. Allen Greer.

On November 1, 1954, Dennis used the heart-lung machine, to which he acknowledged Zuhdi made specific contributions, as a mechanical assisted circulation device to a failing heart. Almost seven months later, on June 30, 1955, Dennis performed his first successful open-heart surgery with the same heart-lung machine. Zuhdi was overwhelmed with the realization that, with Dennis, the medical landscape of the world had been forever changed through the bifurcation of total body perfusion into open heart surgery and mechanical assistance to failing hearts.

In remembering Zuhdi as a resident, Dennis said, "During his training at Brooklyn, Zuhdi was a very bright star among the 50-odd residents in training there, always ready with suggestions and the drive to carry them through, which he did regularly in the year he worked with me in the research laboratory during our work on developing a pump-oxygenator, as a result of which we were able to salvage the first long-term survivor of massive myocardial infarction and shock by temporary circulatory support with that same pump-oxygenator."

To complete the dynamic events of the first five years of the 1950s, the treatment of heart disease was revolutionized. Following, in March, 1955, Dr. John Kirklin at the Mayo Clinic in Rochester, Minnesota, performed a successful open-heart surgery with the aid of a modified Gibbon heart-lung machine. On July 12, 1955, Dr. C. Walton Lillehei, with whom Dr. Zuhdi later studied at the University of Minnesota, performed a successful open heart surgery with his DeWall-Lillehei heart-lung machine.

During the period of 1950 to 1955, there were only five scientists/physicians in the world who were persistent in the development of open-heart surgery and the use of mechanical assistance to a failing heart. They were Dr. Dennis, Dr. Gibbon, Dr. Lillehei, Dr. Kirklin, and Dennis' trainee and the youngest of the pioneers, Dr. Zuhdi. Zuhdi's colleagues encouraged him to follow his passion and vision.

Already an internationally-recognized and sought after surgeon and scientist, in 1957 Zuhdi was recruited by Dr. John Schilling, one of only three department chiefs, to come to Oklahoma and the

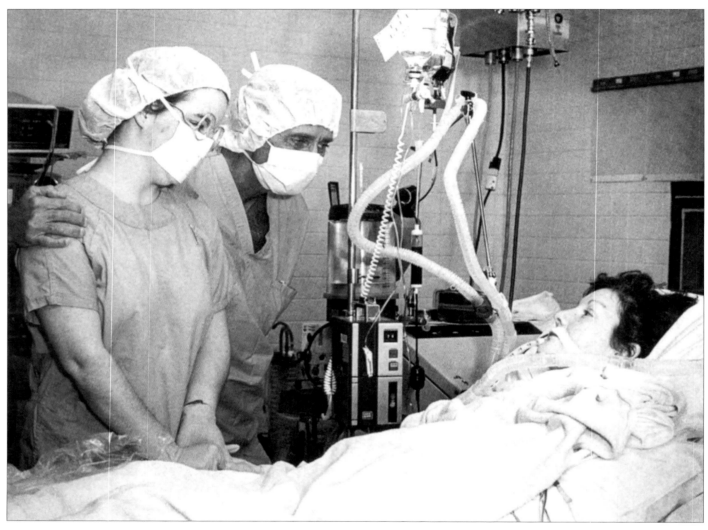

Nancy Rogers in the recovery room after her heart transplant on March 4, 1985.

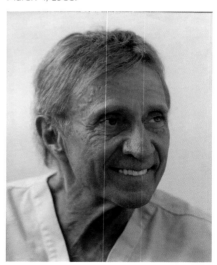

Dr. Nazih Zuhdi.

University of Oklahoma College of Medicine. OU officials believed his presence would improve the medical school's national reputation. Zuhdi relocated and built his experimental laboratory in the basement of the medical school library.

After a year, Zuhdi moved his laboratory to the aging community 13th Street Mercy Hospital just north of downtown Oklahoma City. He spent long hours in his laboratory, perfecting new ways to use total body perfusion, the heart-lung machine, mechanical assistance to the heart, and transplantation. In 1959, with Dr. Allen Greer and Dr. John Carey, Zuhdi performed the first heart bypass operation and installed the first pacemaker in Oklahoma.

Often, Zuhdi was tempted to leave Oklahoma for other medical research centers in the nation because he faced stiff opposition from many physicians who did not appreciate his unique personality and unique methods of "doing his own thing" in a hospital/research setting. Two Oklahoma City civic leaders were vital in urging him to stay. Oilman John Kirkpatrick who, with the Sisters of Mercy and Greer, Carey & Zuhdi, Inc., helped build Zuhdi's Mercy Hospital experimental laboratory and brought in Navy engineer Clark Ritchie from Washington, D.C. to help Zuhdi in his artificial heart work. In the hallway at Mercy, publisher E.K. Gaylord greeted Zuhdi and, with a firm handshake, stated simply, "Stay, you are an Oklahoman."

In February, 1960, Zuhdi, his research in continuum from 1952 to 1959, realized the discovery of total body perfusion and called it Total Intentional Hemodilution (TIH), the priming of a heart-lung machine without blood. TIH changed the future of medical treatment for the human heart, as well as all organs, a fact recognized by the other leading heart treatment pioneers. Open-heart surgery now was possible on a scale never before imagined. Hemodilution became standard procedure in

hospitals around the globe. Dr. Kirklin said, "Dr. Zuhdi has been working in the field of open heart surgery virtually since its beginning. His major contributions were made quite a long time ago and, therefore today, seem almost 'conventional wisdom.'"

Years later, during an interview with Jane Fried of *Public Medical News*, Prof. Herbert Warden at the University of West Virginia said, "Total Intentional Hemodilution divided open-heart surgery into two eras—the pre-Zuhdi era and the post-Zuhdi era."

Zuhdi looked for a new opportunity to expand his research and treatment of heart patients. He chose the infant prairie hospital, Baptist Medical Center. He remembered, "I saw great possibilities to make substantial progress at Baptist. I wanted to demonstrate the elevation of a community hospital to compete with university hospitals and go beyond."

Dr. Zuhdi performed the first open-heart surgery at BMC on April 1, 1963, assisted by Dr. Carey. In 1970, at Baptist Medical Center, Zuhdi implanted a Carpentier Glutaraldehyde porcine aortic valve in a patient, the first such procedure performed in

Members of the surgical transplantation team at BMC in 1987, left to right, Dr. John Chaffin, Dr. David Cooper, chief surgeon Dr. Nazih Zuhdi, Dr. Allen Greer, and Dr. Dimitri Novitzky.

Dr. Nazih Zuhdi, right, and heart transplant pioneer Dr. Christiaan Barnard were honored by the Kiowa Tribe for their contributions to human life. Zuhdi and Barnard were co-trainees in Dr. C. Walton Lillehei's heart services at the University of Minnesota in 1956. Barnard made his home in South Africa and Zuhdi in Oklahoma. Barnard later described employing "...the heart lung machine...using the Hemodilution technique developed by my longtime friend and colleague Nazih Zuhdi..."

North America. Later, following collaboration with scientist Warren Hancock, Zuhdi implanted the first *stabilized* Glutaraldehyde porcine aortic valve in the world.

Dr. Zuhdi's research and development of new machines and methods to treat the human heart have earned worldwide recognition. His is the only medical research conducted within the boundaries of Oklahoma that is recognized in *World's Who's Who In Science: A Biographical Dictionary of Notable Scientists from Antiquity to the Present,* a leading publication edited by the respected Allen G. Debus, then professor of the History of Science at the University of Chicago, his three associates, and an advisory council representing 20 of the most respected universities in science. The story of Dr. Zuhdi's pioneering research, surgeries, and transplants appear in the book alongside biographical sketches of historic scientists such as Galileo, Sir Isaac Newton, Louis Pasteur, Albert Einstein, Charles Darwin, and Thomas Edison. It is noted that Dr. Zuhdi's hyphothermic hemodilution technique was used by Dr. Christiaan Barnard in the world's first human heart transplant in 1967. For years, Dr. Zuhdi frequently performed open-heart surgeries and leading heart physicians and scientists traveled to Oklahoma City to observe his work.

Dr. Zuhdi became the first chairman of the Oklahoma Heart Center. On May 12, 1984, the Center was dedicated and the keynote speech was given by Zuhdi's friend, Dr. Christiaan Barnard. Both Zuhdi and Barnard had been fellows of Dr. C. Walton Lillehei in Minnesota in 1956.

Following a stellar career in South Africa, Barnard was appointed scientist in residence by Zuhdi and joined him in Oklahoma City. The two sometimes rode in a specially-equipped bus to carry the message throughout Oklahoma about the exciting future of organ transplants. Barnard's role was as an advisor and public relations officer for the Oklahoma Heart Center.

In November, 1984, Dr. Zuhdi, operating without the knowledge of BMC administration, created the Oklahoma Transplant Institute as the venue for organ transplantation. It was Zuhdi's program, Zuhdi's alone. He set out to select the right physicians, scientists, technicians, and nurses to staff the new transplantation program. His vision was to create one cohesive unit for all solid organ transplants—heart, kidney, lung, liver, pancreas, and small bowel. It would be the first facility in the world to develop such a program. It was not a popular decision.

Although BMC chairman Kenneth Bonds, Jay Henry, and Dr. Thomas Lynn believed in Dr. Zuhdi's vision, few other board members and physicians supported the innovative effort and creation of the transplantation institute. A host of physicians signed a petition asking Zuhdi to take his experiments elsewhere. Fortunately, for history's sake, Dr. Bobby Gene Smith tore the petition into many small parts and urged Zuhdi to continue. It was not unfamiliar territory for Zuhdi. His archivist and biographer, Brooks Barr, wrote, "Zuhdi knew what it was to be alone in the ocean, paddling madly for a shore yet unseen, for he had likewise been stranded in the lifeboat with Dennis and Lillehei before."

Another new era in medicine in Oklahoma began in the early morning hours of March 4, 1985. Dr. Zuhdi performed the state's first human-to-human heart transplant and the first such procedure in the nation in a hospital not associated with a medical school.

Earlier, Dr. Zuhdi had dispatched resident Dr. David Vanhooser, whom he had taught how to retrieve the heart, medical student John Zweicker, and nurses Pat Sumpter and Cheryl Montgomery to Georgia to remove the heart of a 14-year-old girl killed in an automobile accident. Back in Oklahoma City, Dr. Zuhdi and his team had begun preparing their patient for the procedure in the late hours of March 3.

In the four-hour operation, 45-year-old Nancy Rogers of Oklahoma City, who was transferred from Mercy Hospital to BMC, received the new heart and a new lease on life. In *The Oklahoman,* Susan Simpson recounted the moment when Dr. Zuhdi connected the transplanted heart and opened the aortic clamp:

> The organ filled with blood. A hush fell over the room as the heart began to warm. Would it beat? Thump thump. Thump thump. The organ contracted. The blood flowed. Smiles erupted behind surgical masks. Oklahoma's first heart transplantation was successful.

The successful transplant continued to raise BMC's international prominence, making it one of 12 or so hospitals in the nation that had performed a heart-transplant and the only community hospital to do so. Reporters from across the world covered the story.

Within a couple of weeks, Rogers, at the invitation of the chairman, attended a meeting of the hospital's board of directors. Medical Director Dr. Thomas Lynn remembered, "She danced down the center aisle and did several pirouettes for her fascinated audience, reinforcing the sense of pride that was universally felt."

Approximately three weeks following surgery Rogers was readmitted to the hospital. Lynn told the press, "There's no sign of rejection, she's got a bug."

High profile celebrities, including Naomi Judd, and Frank Sinatra, appeared at benefits to raise money for the Oklahoma Transplant Institute. Sinatra, right, with Nazih and Annette Zuhdi at a benefit held at the Lloyd Noble Center in Norman.

Dr. Nazih Zuhdi describing to the board the first heart transplant performed at Baptist Medical Center.

Dr. Max Edgar was the staff psychologist of the Oklahoma Transplant Institute from its inception in 1984.

The "bug," cytomegalovirus opportunistic infection, rapidly attacked Rogers' body and she died 54 days after her successful transplant surgery. The anti-viral drugs we have today to control such a virus did not exist in the 1980s. Today, heart transplant patients may live for decades, thanks to discoveries of new anti-rejection and anti-infection drugs.

Rogers was the first heart transplant at BMC and in Oklahoma in 1985. The 500th heart transplant was celebrated in February, 2014. NZTI remains the only center in the state of Oklahoma performing heart transplants, as well as lung transplants.

In a short time, OTI scored more firsts. Still in 1985, Dr. Zuhdi performed a Piggyback/Tandem heart transplant, the first in Oklahoma, and only the sixth in the nation. *USA Today* and other national publications were interested in what was happening at BMC. After Zuhdi appeared on ABC's "Good Morning America," *Friday* newspaper publisher, J. Leland Gourley, wrote, "This is the kind of achievement that will help Oklahoma in its new drive for more high tech industry."

With Zuhdi as Surgeon-in-Chief, he began the search for qualified surgeons and scientists for the transplantation institute. British surgeon, Dr. David Cooper, who participated in London's first heart transplant, became Director of Research and Education. Dr. John Chaffin became a primary

The popular football coaches at the University of Oklahoma and Oklahoma State University helped promote organ donation and the Oklahoma Transplant Institute in 1987 in celebration of the 20th anniversary of Dr. Christiaan Barnard's first human heart transplant using Zuhdi's Total Intentional Hemodilution.

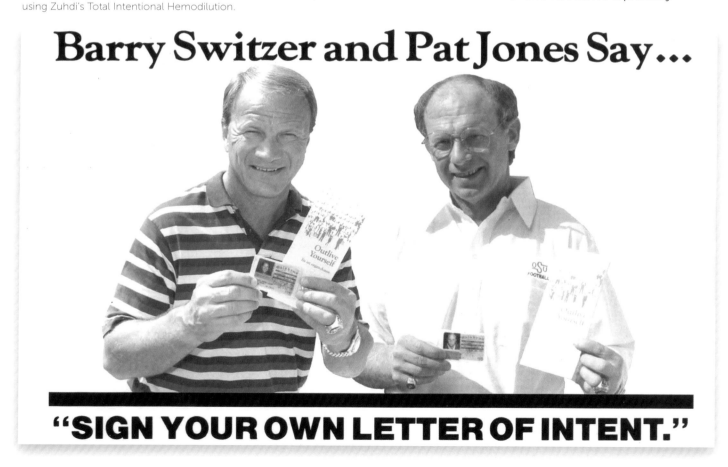

Barry Switzer and Pat Jones Say...

"SIGN YOUR OWN LETTER OF INTENT."

transplant surgeon. Dr. David Vanhooser, a thoracic surgeon who had retrieved the heart for the first Oklahoma heart transplant, became a member of the Institute team. The nucleus, of course, also included Zuhdi's longtime partner, Dr. Allen Greer.

The quest for excellence in BMC's transplant activity was further enhanced when Zuhdi recruited Dr. David VanTheil, and members of his team, from the University of Pittsburgh. VanTheil established the protocols for liver transplantations. He brought with him hundreds of blood, tissue, and cell samples that needed specialized conditions to preserve them. The Oklahoma Medical Research Foundation collaborated with OTI to perform the lab work for future successful transplant surgeries. Dr. Scott Samara was named Chief of the kidney transplant division of the Transplantation Institute.

On June 4, 1987, Zuhdi and Dr. Dimitri Novitzky performed Oklahoma's first human heart-lung transplant.

In the same year, Zuhdi implanted the state's first left ventricular assist device and Dr. Scott Samara performed OTI's first kidney transplant. In 1988, Zuhdi implanted the state's first left ventricular assist device and right ventricular assist device in a patient awaiting a heart transplant. Four months later a heart became available and the transplant was a success.

Zuhdi helped develop the Oklahoma Organ Sharing Network, a program designed to educate the public about organ donation and coordinate the availability and transplantation of all organs. In 1990, Zuhdi performed the state's first single-lung transplant. Betty Phillips of Oklahoma City suffered from chronic pulmonary emphysema for 11 years and had spent the last two years with an oxygen tank at her side. When the call came that a donor lung had been found, Dr. Chaffin flew to Houston, Texas, to retrieve the organ. Assisting Dr. Zuhdi were Drs. Greer, Cooper, and Chaffin.

Oklahoma Governor Frank Keating signed a bill into law in April, 1998, that provided that organs donated in Oklahoma first be offered to Oklahoma patients needing transplants. Left to right, behind the governor, are Senator Angela Monson, Dr. James Whiteneck, Lieutenant Governor Mary Fallin, Robert Turner, Representative Bill Paulk, and Dr. Nazih Zuhdi. Governors Keating and Brad Henry later bestowed on Zuhdi a proclamation and commendation respectively acknowledging Zuhdi's many contributions to Oklahoma and the world.

Cutting the ribbon at the August, 1999 opening of the Nazih Zuhdi Transplant Institute are, left to right, Bruce Lawrence, Josephine Freede, Dr. Nazih Zuhdi, Edward Joullian, Dr. Bakr Nour, and Stan Hupfeld.

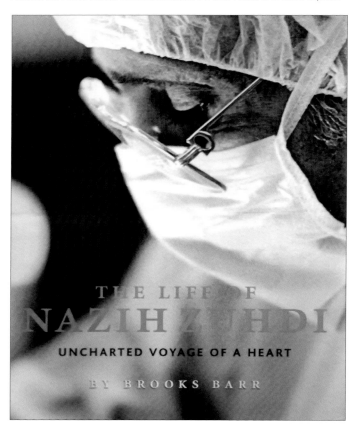

THE LIFE OF NAZIH ZUHDI

UNCHARTED VOYAGE OF A HEART

BY BROOKS BARR

The comprehensive biography of Dr. Nazih Zuhdi, *The Life of Nazih Zuhdi: Uncharted Voyage of a Heart,* was published by Oklahoma Heritage Association Publishing, a publication of the Oklahoma Hall of Fame, in 2005.

With the heart and lung transplant program well underway, Zuhdi forged ahead with a liver transplant regimen at OTI. Hupfeld prepared a detailed presentation for the hospital board of directors and told Zuhdi that he must hold his remarks to only five minutes of the 45 minutes allocated for the presentation. After all, there was much information for the board to digest in order to approve an aggressive liver transplant program.

When Hupfeld asked Zuhdi to introduce the program, his first words were, "I am Nazih Zuhdi—son of Abraham." Zuhdi spent ten minutes reviewing the relationship of Christians, Muslims, and Jews. For another ten minutes he talked about his childhood. After another 20 minutes detailing his early training, Hupfeld thought, "We are 45 minutes into an agenda item slated for five and the story of Nazih Zuhdi still has not made it to the United States."

Hupfeld informed the board of two options—Dr. Zuhdi could be invited back next month, or the liver transplant program could be approved without further discussion. Within seconds, the motion was made and approved to launch the liver transplantation regimen. Hupfeld remembered, "The board clearly was very comfortable with embarking on something this serious if they were convinced that Nazih Zuhdi was committed to the program. They had seen him too many times perform miracles."

In 1992, Dr. Luis Mieles and Dr. Hadar Merhav performed Oklahoma's first liver transplant. Jay Dysart, a 31-year-old man from Tipton, Oklahoma, received a new liver and left BMC in excellent condition.

Also in 1992, the Oklahoma Transplant Institute was ranked first in Oklahoma and second in the nation in survival of heart transplant patients of hospitals performing more than 50 transplant procedures. The United States Department of Health and Human Services reported that out of 56 heart transplants, OTI had a survival rate of 89.3 percent. OTI's high survival rate was realized despite the fact that 41 percent of the heart transplant patients were on life support prior to their transplant surgery compared to 18 percent nationwide. Dr. Zuhdi gave the credit to "the knowledge and dedication of the physicians, nurses, technicians, and support members in our program."

In 1993, Dr. Merhav performed a liver transplant and Dr. Scott Samara performed a kidney transplant in the state's first liver/kidney transplant procedure. In 1994, Zuhdi performed Oklahoma's first double-lung transplant and Dr. Bakr Nour performed Oklahoma's first pediatric liver transplant at OTI. In 1995, Dr. Nour and Dr. Eliezer Katz performed the first living-related liver transplant in the state and Dr. Anthony Sebastian and Dr. Samara teamed to perform Oklahoma's first kidney/pancreas transplant.

In 1996, Dr. Katz and Dr. Myron Schwartz of the Mount Sinai Medical Center in New York City, performed the nation's first in-situ split-liver transplant. The same year, Dr. Nour performed Oklahoma's first small bowel transplant.

In 1997, Dr. Sebastian performed Oklahoma's first pancreas-liver transplant and Dr. Vanhooser implanted the first Heart-Mate brand left ventricular assist device. In 1998, Dr. Vanhooser and Dr. Chaffin performed the Oklahoma Transplant Institute's 1,000th solid organ transplant, a heart transplant procedure.

In 1999, Dr. Zuhdi officially retired and chose his successor Dr. Bakr Nour as director of the transplant institute, renamed the Nazih Zuhdi Transplant Institute (NZTI).

In 2002, a new liver dialysis machine was added to the arsenal of equipment available at NZTI, the state's only comprehensive transplant center. For many on the waiting list for liver donors, the wait was lengthy. An exception was Judy McNerney, a retired Oklahoma City school teacher, who was told she might have to wait a year for a new liver. However, eight days after she entered the transplantation program, McNerney received a liver from a donor in Tulsa.

Part of the mission of NZTI was to better inform the public of the value of donating organs to

The bust of Dr. Nazih Zuhdi by sculptor Shan Gray stands at the entrance to the Nazih Zuhdi Transplant Institute in the IBMC main lobby. Also in the lobby are granite monoliths listing Zuhdi's contributions to the world of medicine.

Todd Begley, right, and his wife, Jennifer. Todd received a liver transplant in 2014.

In 2002, the organs of an Elk City boy gave new life to four ailing Oklahomans. Michelle Cogburn, left, talks about her son, Justin, age 16, who died in April, 2002. At right is Jerral Evans of Ponca City who was given the teen's pancreas and a kidney. *Courtesy Oklahoma Publishing Company.*

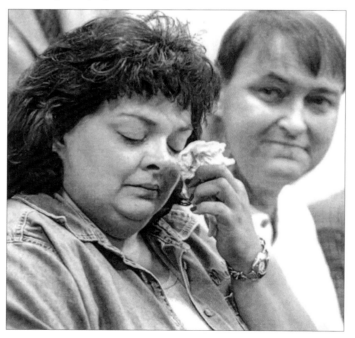

sustain life in others. After Oklahoma Corporation Commissioner Ed Apple donated a kidney to his friend, James Metzer, in 2002, Metzer wrote *The Oklahoman:*

> I thank God we have such a wonderful transplant center in our own city. My prayer is that God will continue to bless them and their marvelous work. Because of them and Ed Apple, my life has been changed forever for the better.

In January, 2003, a Del City woman, became the 500th liver transplant patient at NZTI, joining organ recipients who traveled to Oklahoma City from as far as Egypt, India, Italy, Turkey, Venezuela, and 25 states.

In 2004, Dr. Johnny Griggs replaced Dr. Nour as Medical Director of NZTI. In 2006, Griggs was succeeded by Dr. Nicolas Jabbour, the first medical director chosen by IBMC administration without Zuhdi's knowledge.

In 2008, the United States Department of Health and Human Services awarded IBMC a Medal of Honor for substantially raising its organ donation rates. The hospital had an organ donation rate of 82 percent, substantially higher than the average rate of 50 percent.

In 2009, a six-way kidney transplant was successfully completed at NZTI. The transplant involving living donors was special for kidney recipient Scott Clark of Moore, Oklahoma, who said it is often bittersweet for patients needing a new kidney because most organs come from deceased donors. He said, "It's a horrible feeling to wait for people to die so you can live." It was the second transplant for Clark who had received a liver from a deceased donor seven years before.

The six-way transplant involved surgeries spread over several weeks. Dr. Scott Samara, and his son, Dr. Shea Samara, and Dr. William Miller, participated.

Fortunately for the thousands of patients who have received organ transplants from NZTI in its more than a quarter century of operation, once almost impossible procedures such as a double-lung transplant have become ordinary. In December, 2009, Lori Red-Ademiuyl received new lungs after suffering chronic shortness of breath and being unable to walk more than a few feet without becoming fatigued. Getting new lungs gave her a new life that allowed her to finally be active with her youngest child.

World renowned cardio-thoracic surgeon and authority on artificial hearts, Dr. James Long, whose association with OTI began in 1994, was named the head of NZTI in 2010. For a number of years,

Far more important than the statistics showing the success of NZTI are the individual stories from organ transplant recipients.

HEART TRANSPLANT

Joe McNutt
As the dye raced through his blood vessels to his heart, Joe McNutt heard the alarmed doctor issue orders to stop the test. "Your heart is gone, Joe," the doctor told him later. "You need a transplant."

Odus Newman
My name is Odus Newman. I live in a small little town called Wapanucka, Oklahoma. I was at work one day and started feeling very badly. At the time I didn't know that I was having a heart attack. I received my new heart one week prior to my birthday. Talk about a good birthday present.

R.V. Reid
My heart attack was on January 2, 1988. On February 25, Dr. Zuhdi told my wife that I had about one day left. I was on machines. That night, on the 25th, I was told that Dr. Cooper was on his way to Dallas to get me a new heart. Close call. Now, 19 years later, I still remember!

KIDNEY TRANSPLANT

Tima Krausse
In August of 2003, my sister, Jan Atchley, donated a kidney to me, allowing me to enjoy a much better quality of life with my children. Words can never express my gratitude for her gift of love to me.

Joan Saint
Way back in 1995 I got my chance for a kidney transplant. This came on a Sunday afternoon. I had been on peritoneal dialysis for less than a year, long enough for me to be comfortable with it.

LIVER TRANSPLANT

Shari England
How do you thank someone when they no longer inhabit the earth? When, if ever, will the opportunity present itself, placing you face to face with the family of the one who gave you the most precious gift one person can give another? What if that opportunity never comes? These are questions I confess I did not contemplate deeply during the months and years prior to my transplant. Now I ponder them almost daily.

Carmen Eppler
On Mother's Day 1997, I received the most precious gift of life with a new liver. While the doctors were telling my family that I may not make it through the night, another family faced the opportunity to donate their loved one's organs. Because of their decision to give, I received a second chance to live.

Carol G. Sheid
I look at life much differently since that day in 1996. Small things are more precious to me. I know that God was not ready for me to leave this earth.

LUNG TRANSPLANT

Rex Williams
I was diagnosed with chronic obstructive pulmonary disease (COPD) when I was 42-years-old and decided I could smoke and drink myself to death before the disease got me. I was wrong.

In 2005, Dr. Nazih Zuhdi, center, celebrated the 20th anniversary of Oklahoma's first heart transplant with Kent Rogers, left, husband of Nancy Rogers, the first heart transplant patient. *Courtesy Oklahoma Publishing Company.*

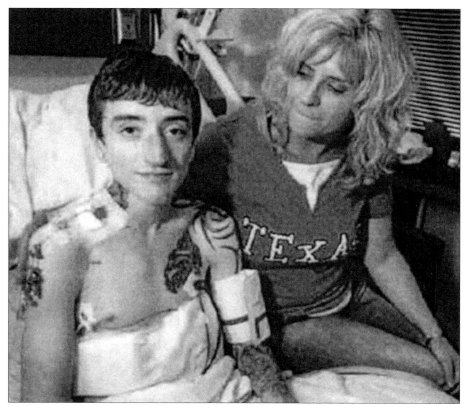

Cody Sheets, a double-lung transplant recipient, with his mother, Terrie Morris, after his August, 2010, transplant at NZTI.

Living-related liver transplant recipient Mark Florie went on to play high school basketball and today is married and the father of two.

Victor Pollack, right, and his wife, Evelyn, talk to reporters about his new HeartMate II implant at IBMC in July, 2008. *Courtesy Oklahoma Publishing Company.*

OKLAHOMA TRANSPLANT INSTITUTE AND NAZIH ZUHDI TRANSPLANT INSTITUTE "FIRSTS"

1985
- First heart transplant in Oklahoma
- First piggyback heart transplant in Oklahoma

1987
- First heart-lung transplant in Oklahoma
- First left ventricular assist device implanted in Oklahoma
- First kidney transplant at NZTI

1988
- First left ventricular assist device and right ventricular assist device implanted in Oklahoma to sustain life until successful transplant (4 mos. later)

1990
- First single lung transplant in Oklahoma

1992
- First liver transplant in Oklahoma

1994
- First double lung transplant in Oklahoma
- First pediatric liver transplant in Oklahoma

1995
- First living-related liver transplant in Oklahoma
- First kidney/pancreas transplant in Oklahoma

1996
- First small bowel transplant in Oklahoma
- NZTI and Mount Sinai Hospital, New York City, leads nation's first in-situ split liver transplant

2008
- First paired kidney transplant in Oklahoma

2009
- NZTI participates with other hospitals in first six-way kidney transplant

2010
- First Levacor heart pump device implanted in the nation

Dr. David Nelson, under Zuhdi's direction, had been developing the infrastructure to bring Long on board.

In June, 2010, Dr. Scott Samara reached a professional milestone by successfully performing his 1,000th kidney transplant at NZTI. He said, "Over the past 37 years [not all at NZTI] I have been a part of an unbelievable journey of this ever-changing medical phenomenon."

In the same month of Dr. Samara's 1,000th kidney transplant, the NZTI Lung Transplant program celebrated 20 years. Dr. Remzi Bag, chief of the INTEGRIS Lung Transplant program, noted that the founders of the program were "forward thinkers." NZTI is still one of only 60 lung transplant facilities in the world.

By 2010, 174 people had benefited from the innovative and often lifesaving lung-transplant program. In August, 2010, 24-year-old Cody Sheets received a double-lung transplant and was able, for the first time, to breathe freely. He had suffered from cystic fibrosis since age two, a disease that causes a thickening of mucous in the lungs and digestive system.

On July 2, 2010, renowned Oklahoma artist Harold T. Holden's life was saved with a single lung transplant. To honor his experience, Holden dedicated to NZTI a recasting of a six-foot sculpture titled "Thank You Lord," which depicts a life-sized cowboy standing with his hat held over his heart, head back facing the heavens, thanking God for his blessings. The inscription on the plaque reads: This sculpture celebrates the Nazih Zuhdi Transplant Institute for its exemplary service and care to patients and families.

Since its opening, NZTI has expanded from a staff of only three to more than 150 clinicians and support personnel. It is recognized as one of the nation's leading transplantation centers. BMC's place in heart treatment history was sealed because of its association with Dr. Zuhdi. INTEGRIS statistician Roy Monlux calculated the global impact of Dr. Zuhdi's development of Total Intentional Hemodilution to be more than $11 trillion in 2010.

Artists William Shirley and Vala Ola unveiled their portrait of Dr. Nazih Zuhdi during events in conjunction with his retirement. The portrait hangs in the lobby of NZTI.

INTEGRIS
Cancer Institute

Henry G. Bennett, Jr.
Fertility Institute

Courtesy Axiz Photography and Toby Nabors

CHAPTER 11

INTEGRIS Cancer Institute

Cancer had become one of the nation's biggest health concerns by the time Baptist Memorial Hospital opened in 1959. Physicians who practiced at the hospital used clinicians in different departments to assist patients who needed treatment for various types of cancer. From the hospital's beginning, the cancer program received full unrestricted approval from the Commission on Cancer. The Cancer Committee became one of the standing committees of the medical center.

Dr. James Hampton helped developed an oncology treatment program in the late 1970s.

The first concentrated effort to develop a thorough cancer treatment program at BMC came in the late 1970s when Dr. James Hampton came from the Oklahoma Medical Research Foundation. He developed an Oncology Rehabilitation Team and the hospital added a nuclear and radiological diagnostic and treatment area, as well as space for chemotherapy. An outpatient oncology program began in 1976 as an alternative to hospitalization for patients needing chemotherapy treatments.

In 1985, the first specialized cancer center was created at BMC and named the Cancer Center of the Southwest. Dr. Hampton was named Medical Director and registered nurse Nancy Burrell was the Center's first director. Dr. Peter Greenwald, director of prevention for the National Cancer Institute, spoke at the dedication of the Cancer Center and announced that the government's goal was to reduce deaths from cancer by 50 percent by 2000.

The Cancer Center concept enabled patients to receive treatment in a centralized area, patient-nurse relationships could develop, and highly-trained nurses could assist patients with side effects that might occur with treatment. In addition to the Cancer Treatment Unit with its adjacent pharmacy, the Hulsey Suite gave patients and families a place to relax and meditate. The Cancer Care Team met weekly to review each patient's progress. Members of the team included nurses, social workers, dietitians, chaplains, patient representatives, pain management specialists, physical therapists, and occupational therapists.

In the early 1990s, the Cancer Center needed more space and new diagnostic equipment to stay current with the treatment of cancer patients. An interested observer was Troy Smith of Shawnee, the founder of Sonic Drive-Ins, the nation's largest chain of its kind. Smith was a cancer survivor himself, having been successfully treated for prostate cancer at the M.D. Anderson Cancer Center in Houston, Texas. He was impressed with the care he received there and felt strongly that such care should be available to Oklahomans closer to home.

Smith and his wife, Dollie, made a generous contribution of $2 million in 1994 to ensure Oklahomans access to the highest-quality, most comprehensive treatment for cancer. It was the largest single donation ever made to Baptist Medical Center. The Smiths' gift provided funds for equipment including a simulator for radiation therapy, a patient learning resource center, cancer registry equipment, prevention trials research, and community education and medical staff lectureships.

In addition, the Smiths created a $1 million research and education endowment to assist the Cancer Center that was renamed the Troy & Dollie Smith Cancer Center. A new library and support center was dedicated to the memory of Bettie Templin, a deeply devoted founding member of the Living Life with Cancer support group at BMC. She built a large personal library of books and tapes for people seeking information about living with cancer.

Part of the mission of the expanded and renovated Smith Cancer Center (SCC) was participation in research trials using National Cancer Institute approved research protocols. Nurse Maxine Watson coordinated a Breast Cancer Prevention Trial with Dr. Karl Boatman serving as oncology researcher for 60 women taking part in the trial. The hospital was chosen as the principal site for a Prostate Cancer Prevention Trial, a seven-year chemo-prevention trial for men over age 55 at risk for developing prostate cancer.

SCC moved far beyond treatment of cancer patients. Support programs were expanded and the Reach to Recovery program was created to meet women's needs immediately after a breast cancer diagnosis. The first Oklahoma camp for adult cancer patients and their families was held. SCC director Terry Gonsoulin outlined the mission of the Center:

> To promote a humanistic environment for both inpatient and outpatient care of persons experiencing cancer and to provide support for their families. Our commitment of caring for the physical as well as emotional components of healing continues.

When the expanded Cancer Center opened, 30 private-bed units were available with registered nurses with special training in oncology. The radiation oncology department was a modern therapeutic treatment facility staffed with two fulltime radiation oncologists, a fulltime radiation physicist, nurse clinician, and two certified medical dosemetrists, and a highly experienced group of radiation therapists. Three high-energy linear accelerators offered a full range of photon and electron energies.

In addition to radiation, other treatment modes available included fine needle aspiration, hepatic chemoembolization, enterostomal therapy, home care, stereotactic biopsy, nurse case management, physical therapy, occupation therapy, pastoral care, individual and family counseling, nutrition services, pain and symptom management, and social work services. A cancer chemotherapy administration course was provided for registered nurses four times a year to allow nurses to acquire advanced knowledge of cancer chemotherapy.

Support groups have been a primary focus of the Cancer Center since its inception. In January, 1994, the Choices Breast Cancer support group was formed for women diagnosed with breast cancer. Choices was an acronym for Companionship, Humor, Optimism, Insight, Courage, Education, and Spirituality, which reminded members that they had control over many choices during their experience with breast cancer.

An inpatient support group, Take Five, met twice weekly. A Cancer Connection volunteer, social worker, and licensed counselor were available to meet individually or with families regarding problems and concerns relating to their illness. Chapter Two was a six-week program offering support for adults coping with grief from the death of a loved one. Calm Waters was available for children coping with loss.

Cancer treatment is now conducted under the umbrella of the INTEGRIS Cancer Institute that includes treatment facilities at INTEGRIS Baptist Medical Center, Southwest Medical Center, and the INTEGRIS Cancer Institute Proton Campus in far northwest Oklahoma City. The Institute's foremost collection of physicians uses state-of-the-art

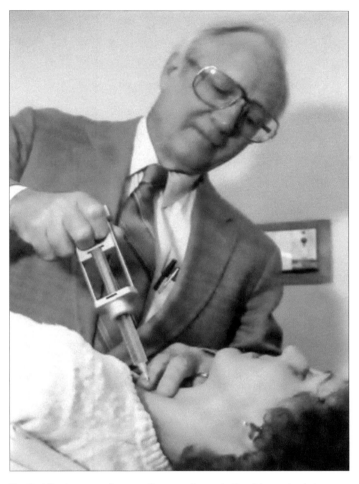

Dr. Karl Boatman performs a fine needle aspiration biopsy to determine whether or not a lump is cancerous.

comprehensive therapies to diagnose and treat cancer patients.

The newest unit of the Cancer Institute was built on 24 acres on the Kilpatrick Turnpike adjacent to the Oklahoma ProCure Treatment Center. The ProCure Center was only the sixth proton center built in the United States. The two are partners, creating a world-class cancer institute that provides services found nowhere else in the region. They complement one another with a multidisciplinary, collaborative approach to cancer care using the most sophisticated equipment of its type in the world.

The 135,000-square-foot INTEGRIS Cancer Center facility in northwest Oklahoma City was dedicated May 13, 2008. Stan Hupfeld said, "As we contemplated an idea for a cancer institute, we felt there were several imperatives. We had to have the best technology available and we needed the best

In the mid-1980s, the Cancer Care Team met weekly to discuss each patient's progress and coordinate their rehabilitation.

Stan Hupfeld presides at the 1994 grand opening of the Troy & Dollie Smith Cancer Center.

Troy and Dollie Smith believed that all Oklahomans should have access to the finest and latest treatments for cancer. Their gift to greatly expand the cancer treatment program at BMC was the largest single donation ever to the hospital.

Outside the INTEGRIS Cancer Institute is a five-foot bronze statue created in the image of Wilma Dockum as a child. She died of cancer as an adult, but her parents, Claude and Opal Huffman, honored her memory with the statue that anchors the Celebration of Life Gardens.

Dr. Sameer Keole, left, raises prostate cancer awareness in a television interview with KFOR-TV's Linda Cavanaugh.

One of the services of the INTEGRIS Cancer Institute is a Look Good...Feel Better program for cancer patients. Susan Adair of Oklahoma City learns makeup and cosmetic tips from Institute staff. *Courtesy Oklahoma Publishing Company.*

physicians to administer treatment."

The INTEGRIS Comprehensive Breast Center is a Food and Drug Administration-accredited facility that offers Digital Mammography with R2 Image Checker, Breast Ultrasound, Breast MRI, and minimally invasive image-guided Breast Biopsy. The Center offers onsite surgical consultation, provides access to genetic testing, and coordinates with the INTEGRIS Cancer Institute to provide patients with counseling services and support groups. In 2009, Dr. Ann Archer, a nationally recognized expert in early detection and prevention of breast cancer, became Medical Director of the Comprehensive Breast Center.

The Troy & Dollie Smith Wellness Center, located inside the Cancer Institute's Proton Campus, is a resource center for patients, their families, and caregivers. Massage, acupuncture, yoga, and art are available in addition to counseling, pastoral care, spiritual support, and cancer registry.

Even though Baptist has provided high quality treatment for cancer patients for more than 50 years, there is a renewed emphasis on innovative modes of treatment. In April, 2010, doctors at IBMC scored another first in Oklahoma, unveiling a new procedure called radioembolization as a safe and effective way to deliver radiation to tumors in the liver. The new treatment protocol allow the injection of small radiation beads into the arterial supply of a tumor, giving 40 times the radiation therapy previously available through external beam radiation.

In June, 2010, the Cancer Institute hosted the 23rd annual National Cancer Survivor's Day Celebration of Life. The special event honored cancer survivors and their families and friends. In addition, the event featured the yearly Celebration of Life Art Exhibit, with art works by people whose lives have been touched by cancer.

Another medical milestone was reached in July, 2010, when Dr. Sameer Keole, Medical Director of the ProCure Proton Therapy Center, worked with a team of physicians, medical physicists, and dosimetrists to develop the first protocol for a range of gastrointestinal treatments with proton therapy. Oklahoma native Dennis Starbuck, age 67, was the first person in the nation to receive proton therapy for anal cancer. Starbuck discovered the possibility of novel treatment through a friend's son who was a member of the construction team that built the Proton Therapy Center.

In September, 2010, the INTEGRIS Cancer Institute expanded its service with Dr. Thomas Showalter providing medical oncology and hematology services at a specialty clinic in Edmond.

INTEGRIS
Heart Hospital

Hough
Ear Institute

Jim Thorpe
Rehabilitation Hospital

Courtesy Axiz Photography and Toby Nabors

CHAPTER 12

Hough Ear Institute

In 1976, Dr. Jack V.D. Hough began work on adult cochlear implantation to restore hearing in the deaf. Dr. Hough was one of only six physicians leading research teams in the nation trying to develop the procedure in which wire electrodes are implanted in the inner ear to stimulate the acoustic nerve. A transmitter worn behind the ear sends impulses through the skin to the electrodes.

In 1978, Dr. Hough went to Baptist Medical Center Administrator Jay Henry to request $100,000 for research that he suggested would literally change the way people were treated for hearing problems. Henry saw the value of the idea and found the requested money in the budget. After the first successful cochlear implant, Henry proposed that the ear institute be founded as a separate non-profit research, educational, and humanitarian service institute.

Thus, the Hough Ear Institute (HEI) was created and ultimately became one of only a handful of facilities in the United States approved by the Federal Drug Administration for cochlear implantation. HEI's mission statement is:

> Guided by Christian principles, the Hough Ear Institute is committed to discovering and implementing new ways to improve hearing and balance to people worldwide through research, education, and service to humanity.

In the spring of 1979, Ray Willingham, a 25-year-old Oklahoma City college student, became one of the first four candidates for cochlear implant surgery at Baptist Medical Center. BMC became only the second center in the nation allowed to perform the operation.

Dr. Hough was joined in his research in 1980 by Dr. Michael McGee, the first American doctor to receive fellowship training at the Hough Ear Institute. After completing the fellowship, McGee became a permanent staff member. He said, "The Institute is a cross between private practice medicine and research. HEI is one of the few places you can do both."

One of Dr. McGee's first contributions to otology was the development of non-ossicle bone grafts for use in middle ear reconstructive surgery. In the mid-1980s, McGee's introduction of non-ossicle grafts dramatically dropped the cost of middle ear reconstruction. Later, another Fellow at HEI, Dr. Graham Bryce, introduced the lathing process which cut preparation time for non-ossicular grafts by another two-thirds.

HEI is the only ear institute in the world to contribute to the research and invention of all of the following—cochlear implants for profound and total deafness, implantable devices for nerve deafness, implantable devices for conductive deafness, and standard hearing aids for less affluent countries.

Some of the noteworthy achievements of HEI include development and introduction of many innovative microscopic surgeries for various ear diseases, design of numerous microscopy surgical instruments, and invention of magnetic coupling

In 1983, Amy Folmar was the first child in Oklahoma, and one of the first in the nation, to receive a surgical electronic cochlear implant.

Dr. Jack V.D. Hough, medical director and founder of the Hough Ear Institute, whispers to patient, Jo Helen Mann, after implantation of a 22-channel cochlear implant, one of the first in the nation.

Dr. Hough and his wife celebrate his 50 years as a physician.

Left to right, Dr. Mary Ann Bauman, Oklahoma First Lady Cathy Keating, Dr. Jack V.D. Hough, and actress Nanette Fabray at a dinner honoring Dr. Hough's contributions to microscopic ear surgery.

for all cochlear implants. The Research and Development Department at HEI emphasizes basic physics and engineering research regarding acoustics and mechanics of the auditory and balance system and on associated designs and development of electromagnetic hearing devices.

Since the 1980s, HEI has collaborated with engineering faculty from the University of Oklahoma and Oklahoma State University. HEI employs engineers, scientists, and technicians with advanced training in auditory physiology, biomedical engineering, physics, and electrical engineering.

From the early days of Dr. Hough's pioneering work, the HEI has functioned in three areas—conceptualize, explore, and develop. All projects began as a concept or a new idea fostered by the Institute's constant exposure to people with hearing problems with no satisfactory solution. There is a close working relationship among doctors, audiologists, and engineering personnel in exchanging ideas,

The Hough Ear Institute is recognized across the nation as a leading treatment and research center in the field of hearing problems.

exploring solutions, and coming up with an answer.

In 1988, Dr. R. Stanley Baker completed a one-year fellowship at HEI and joined Drs. Hough and McGee in the practice. In 1994, Dr. R. Kent Dyer, Jr., joined the team, followed by Dr. Mark Wood in 1995.

HEI is affiliated with the INTEGRIS Baptist Medical Center Cochlear Implant Clinic, the Hearing Enrichment Language Program, Otologic Medical Clinic Inc., and Audio Recovery Inc. Doctors who practice at the Otologic Medical Clinic located on the HEI campus just south of Baptist Medical Center, volunteer their time to do research at HEI. They are looking for the best methods and treatments for the hearing impaired. Doctors and other scientists at HEI are highly regarded and are often consulted by their pears throughout the United States.

In 1994, the Hearing Enrichment Language Program (HELP) was created as a comprehensive program teaching children with hearing loss and their families to listen and talk. The outcomes of children in the program have improved significantly over the years. The importance of the program is documented by the fact that approximately 250 children are born in Oklahoma each year with a severe to profound hearing loss and six percent, or 2,500 children, will have some degree of measurable hearing loss. Dr. Richard Kopke, CEO of HEI, said, "The HELP program is the leader in the state in promoting early identification of hearing loss in children and making available technological advances to aid them in living a normal life."

In 2008, Dr. Donald L. Ewert joined HEI from his post as Associate Vice President for Research at the Oklahoma Medical Research Foundation. As Director of Research Administration at HEI, Ewert assumed major responsibility in the development of the ground floor research center. Generous donors to HEI made the expansion of research facilities possible.

In 2010, HEI partnered with Otologic Pharmaceutics, a private company, in development of a pill to treat hearing loss. The drug combination therapy for noise-induced hearing loss was developed by scientists at HEI and the Oklahoma Medical Research Foundation and began the extensive process of trials with hopes of eventual commercialization.

HEI founder, Dr. Hough, retired as chairman of the board in 2011. He was succeeded by Steve Trice, founder of Jasco Products Company.

In 2012, doctors at HEI developed a medicine that can protect a soldier's hearing in a war zone. Dr. Donald Ewert said the new drug can allow a soldier to carry a pill with him and administer it to himself when the need arises.

In 2008, at the unveiling of a large portrait of Dr. Hough, center, were, left to right, Drs. Stan Baker, Mark Wood, Michael McGee, Richard Kopke, Perry Santos, and Kent Dyer.

HOUGH EAR INSTITUTE ACHIEVEMENTS

First cochlear implantation of a child under age three

First successful cochlear implant in a totally deaf
and totally blind patient

Pioneer development and co-investigation of
multi-channel cochlear implants

Invention and development of the Xomed Audiant
Bone Conductor using inductive coupling for restoration
of hearing in conductive deafness

First human implantation of an electromagnetic implantable
hearing device for sensorineural hearing impairment

Helped build the first all-digital hearing aid in Oklahoma

INTEGRIS
Cancer Institute

Henry G. Bennett, Jr.
Fertility Institute

M. J. and S. Elizabeth Schwartz
Sleep Disorders C

Courtesy Axiz Photography and Toby Nabors

CHAPTER 13

Henry G. Bennett, Jr. Fertility Institute

The Henry G. Bennett, Jr., Fertility Institute was named after the first Chief of Staff of Baptist Medical Center. The beloved Dr. Bennett was trained in gynecology at Johns Hopkins and literally hand-picked doctors for the new Baptist Memorial Hospital in 1959.

Ashton Edwards was the first in vitro fertilization baby born at Baptist Medical Center. Born in December, 1986, Ashton was the daughter of Mary Ann Eckstein and television newsman Brad Edwards.

The Institute opened in 1985, a year after Dr. Bennett died. At the dedication, his fellow resident, Dr. Howard Jones, reviewed Dr. Bennett's lasting dedication to high ethical standards in assisted reproductive technology.

Dr. David A. Kallenberger was the first director of the Institute. Other physicians who formed the core of the new venture were Dr. Royice Everett, Dr. Michael Seikel, Dr. Tony Puckett, and Dr. Fenton Sanger.

BMC's first in vitro fertilization (IFV) baby, Ashton Edwards, was born in December, 1986. IFV is a form of assisted reproductive technology that involves combining eggs and sperm in the laboratory and transferring the fertilized eggs, embryos, into the uterus. After the first IVF baby was born in England in 1978, the procedure became an integral part of infertility treatment. The Ashton Edwards event was much publicized for several reasons. It was a novel medical story and the baby's father was popular television newscaster Brad Edwards.

In April, 1988, Rebecca Smith of Jet, Oklahoma, gave birth to the first set of Oklahoma twins born as a result of a fertility technique called gamete intra-fallopian transfer (GIFT). The fertility procedure had

The medical staff at the Bennett Fertility Institute in 1986. Left to right, Dr. David Kallenberger, Dr. Michael Seikel, Dr. Tony Puckett, Dr. Fenton Sanger, and Dr. Royice Everett.

been performed at the Bennett Fertility Institute by Dr. Kallenberger. The procedure involved surgically removing mature eggs from the mother's ovaries and placing the eggs and sperm in one of her fallopian tubes.

The Smiths had been seeing Dr. Puckett at the Institute for three years and were given odds of only 30 percent success for the new procedure. The parents were warned of the possibility of multiple births if the procedure proved successful.

The state's first set of quintuplets were born at IBMC in September, 1998. Three boys and two girls were born to Jim and Rachelle Goodin. Dubbed the Goodin quintuplets, media outlets covered their stay in the hospital which was more than a month because of their tiny birth weights ranging from three to four pounds. The mother had received a combination of intrauterine insemination and injections of a fertility drug to become pregnant.

Dr. Kallenberger, the Institute's Program Director, was joined in the late 1980s by Dr. Eli Reshef, now the Medical Director of the Bennett Fertility Institute. Both are recognized as experts in their field and teach at the University of Oklahoma College of Medicine. Dr. Kalleberger is chairman of the

Dr. Fenton Sanger counsels a patient in the Fertility Institute in 1986.

Medical Director Dr. David Kallenberger performs a laser laparoscopy to detect endometriosis, a common cause of infertility.

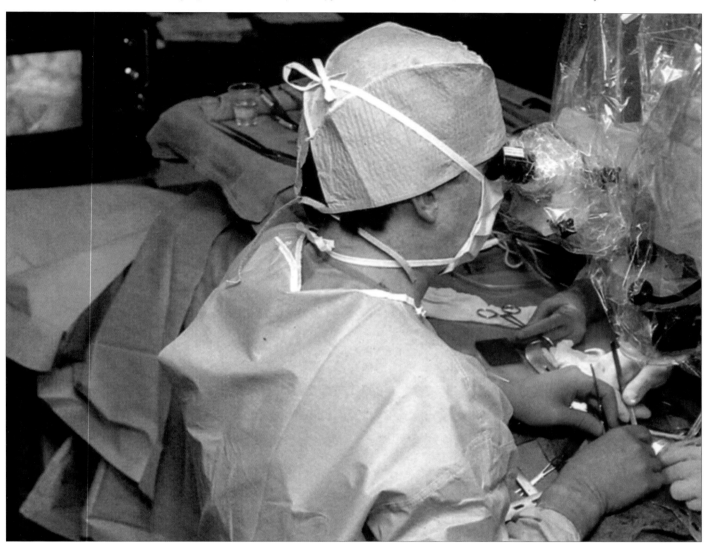

The Fertility Institute's first in vitro fertilization baby, Ashton Edwards, center, at age 19 in 2005. Left to right, Eli Reshef, M.D.; J.W. Edward Wortham, Jr. PhD; Ashton Edwards; David A. Kallenberger, M.D.; and J. Clark Bundren, M.D.

Department of Obstetrics and Gynecology at IBMC.

The Institute has done much to educate Oklahomans about assisted reproductive technology (ART), the high-technology approach to infertility that has not responded to traditional treatments such as fertility pills. Several sophisticated procedures are offered at the Institute to help couples conceive babies, including IVF, micromanipulation, embryo and sperm cryopreservation (freezing and banking), and egg and embryo donation.

Since the Institute opened, thousands of infertile couples have fulfilled their dreams of building families. Dr. Reshef said, "By combining compassionate care with detailed technical instructions, we can alleviate some of the high anxiety and stress among our patients." Dr. Kallenberger said, "Our patients are highly educated and require and deserve much attention. Even our laboratory technicians closely interact with patients. It allows our technicians to interact with real patients, not only with test tubes and Petri dishes."

To make couples feel at home in the Institute's surroundings, Dr. Kallenberger's wife, Jenny, encouraged the display of Oklahoma art on the walls. Prominent local artists donated photography, paintings, and other media to echo themes of fertility and parenthood. Art adorns the walls from the waiting room to examination rooms. The collection is called "Art for ART."

The Institute's success rate is phenomenal. In recent years, it placed among the top fertility programs in the nation according to statistics released by the Society for Assisted Reproductive Technology. Year after year, the Institute ranks in the top five percent in successful treatment of infertility. In 2007, 60 percent of the Institute's patients under age 35 and 58 percent of women from 35 to 37 had babies with IVF attempts. Nationally, only 40 percent of fertilization attempts result in pregnancy.

Dr. Kallengberger explained the high success rate:

> Our clinic has been in operation since 1985 and, therefore, has had the opportunity to acquire vast experience in the art and science of in vitro fertilization. We treat each patient individually, and have a superb laboratory crew to take care of the intricate details of the fertilization and embryo-culture process.

Not only have leaders of the Bennett Fertility Institute reached a high level of excellence in treatment of infertility, they have been involved in the overall effort to increase Oklahoma couples' ability to conceive. In 2010, Dr. Reshef and other fertility experts actively opposed a bill in the Oklahoma legislature that would make it unlawful to compensate egg donors. Dr. Reshef and his colleagues were instrumental in coordinating efforts to educate members of the state legislature about the proposed legislation's detrimental effects on family building.

In 2012, Dr. Reshef received two prestigious national awards, the Hope Award for Advocacy, from the National Infertility Association, and the Suheil Muasher Distinguished Service Award of the American Society for Reproductive Medicine.

Henry G. Bennett, Jr.
Fertility Institute

M. J. and S. Elizabeth Schwartz
Sleep Disorders Center

Courtesy Axiz Photography and Toby Nabors

CHAPTER 14

M.J. and S. Elizabeth Schwartz Sleep Disorders Center

In 2008, the Sleep Disorders Clinic at INTEGRIS Baptist Medical Center was named a Center of Excellence for M.J. and S. Elizabeth Schwartz, the parents of Dr. Jonathan R.L. Schwartz, Medical Director of the clinic. However, treatment for sleep disorders at the medical center had been offered for many years.

Dr. Schwartz, a board certified pulmonologist for more than two decades, is an often-quoted sleep expert in state newspapers. In 2002, IBMC was chosen as one of only 30 hospitals in the nation to participate in a nationwide research study to explore potential treatments for "shift work sleep disorder," a common malady affecting people who regularly work the "graveyard shift," between 10:00 p.m. and 8:00 a.m.

The intense effort to properly treat serious sleep disorders at IBMC began after Dr. Schwartz and others saw less than adequate traditional treatment. He said, "Patients often tell their doctors that they are tired, run down, less energetic. They are frequently given antidepressants and are not asked about the quality or quantity of their sleep."

There are more than 80 sleep disorders. The most common treated at the Schwartz Center are obstructive sleep apnea, insomnia, restless leg syndrome, narcolepsy, and other disorders that cause excessive sleepiness during the day. Even children can suffer from sleep disorders.

Dr. Schwartz has been quoted in many media stories about snoring. "It is no laughing matter," he said. "Snoring may be a signal that something is seriously wrong with the snorer's breathing during sleep." Snoring is often a first indication of potentially life-threatening sleep apnea.

In 2006, Dr. Schwartz was chosen by the American College of Chest Physicians to receive a Humanitarian Award on behalf of himself and other medical volunteers from IBMC who give their time at the Baptist Community Clinic at Olivet Baptist Church.

The Schwartz Center is one of four locations of the INTEGRIS Sleep Disorders Center of Oklahoma. In addition to IBMC, sleep disorders are treated at INTEGRIS Southwest Medical Center, Yukon Sleep Disorders Center, and Sleep Disorders Centers of Oklahoma-Edmond, a department of IBMC.

The Sleep Disorders Center is the only sleep center in Oklahoma with all locations accredited by the American Academy of Sleep Medicine. In 2010, there were only nine sleep disorder centers in the United States with all locations accredited.

Dr. Schwartz and a staff of registered polysomnographic technologists conduct and review sleep studies, a simple outpatient procedure that monitors aspects of a person's sleep and gives the experts critical information required to diagnose and treat sleep disorders.

In 2010, Dr. Schwartz continued the Schwartz Center's commitment to educating the community about sleep disorders by participating in the first annual African American Men's Health Summit, sponsored by INTEGRIS Men's Health University and the East Zion District Men's Association. It was part of a community effort to provide free health and wellness check ups.

The Sleep Disorders Clinic uses a variety of methods, including all-night monitoring to diagnose and treat sleep disorders.

Ear Institute

Jim Thorpe
Rehabilitation Hospital

Courtesy Axiz Photography and Toby Nabors

CHAPTER 15

Jim Thorpe Rehabilitation

An important Center of Excellence at INTEGRIS Baptist Medical Center is Jim Thorpe Rehabilitation. The IBMC inpatient and outpatient rehabilitation units are part of INTEGRIS Jim Thorpe Rehabilitation, Oklahoma's foremost system of inpatient, outpatient, and community-based rehabilitative care for children and adults with traumatic brain injury, stroke, brain tumor, spinal cord injury, amputations, or orthopedic conditions.

The INTEGRIS Baptist Medical Center Volunteer Auxiliary provides numerous opportunities for patients.

In addition to the facilities at IBMC, Jim Thorpe Rehabilitation includes a three-story inpatient facility adjacent to Southwest Medical Center in Oklahoma City and units at Clinton Regional Hospital and Comanche County Memorial Hospital in Lawton. The five main programs include orthopedic outpatient rehabilitation, neurological outpatient rehabilitation, hand rehabilitation, Bright Path pediatric rehabilitation, and lymphedema management.

The rehabilitation program is named for Oklahoma's most famous athlete, Jim Thorpe, who was praised as the "world's greatest athlete" for the first half of the twentieth century. In addition to becoming world famous for his exploits in the 1912 Olympic Games, he was a professional baseball and football star and was the first president of the National Football League. His statue greets visitors at the National Football Hall of Fame in Canton, Ohio.

The Jim Thorpe Rehabilitation inpatient services occupy two floors of IBMC, The outpatient facility is located at 5300 North Independence, one block south of the medical center.

Since its founding in 1986, Jim Thorpe Rehabilitation has provided treatment for more than 40,000 patients and is recognized as one of the nation's largest and most respected facilities of its kind. Physical therapists, occupational therapists, and speech/language pathologists provide specialized treatment for patients. Therapies includes spine mobilization, neuromuscular, reeducation, prosthetic training, and balance disorder. For younger patients, a pediatric clinic at INTEGRIS Baptist Medical Center is staffed by specialists in pediatrics and trained in neurodevelopmental treatment techniques, sensory integration therapy, therapeutic listening, voice, swallowing, cognition, and language needs.

Courtesy Axiz Photography and Toby Nabors

Pioneer Governing Board member R.C. Howard, Jr., left, and Volunteer Auxiliary president Virgie Barrett.

HOSPITAL ADMINISTRATORS/PRESIDENTS

John Hendricks	1959-1960
James L. Henry, FACHE	1961-1986
Stanley F. Hupfeld, FACHE	1987-2000
C. Bruce Lawrence, FACHE	2000-2007
Chris M. Hammes, FACHE	2007-2012
Tim Johnsen	2013-

CHAIRMEN OF BOARD OF DIRECTORS

R.H. Nicholson	1959-1965
R.C. Howard, Jr.	1966-1970
Edwin Watts	1977-1978
W. Kenneth Bonds	1979-1987
James R. Daniel	1988-1990
John E. "Gene" Torbett	1991-1992
Dr. Lee Holden	1993-1995
Robert A. Gregory	1996-1998
John E. "Gene" Torbett	1999-2001
Kent Humphries	2002-2003
Joey D. Sager	2004-2006
Dr. John Huff	2007
H. Edward DeBee	2008-2009
Chris Turner	2010-2012
Alvin Bates	2013-

CHAIRMEN OF INTEGRIS HEALTH

Luke Corbett	2010
Ed Townsend	2011
Marshall Snipes	2012
David Thompson	2015

MEDICAL STAFF OFFICERS

From the beginning, Baptist Hospital maintained a professional organization of doctors that not only looked after their interests, but assured high standards in the delivery of health care services. The doctors recognized that acute health care is a partnership between doctor and hospital. The doctor cannot afford to maintain the sophisticated facilities necessary for modern treatment, and the hospital has no customers—its patients—without the doctor.

In its first half century, there have been only four chiefs of staff at Baptist Medical Center, with Dr. Henry G. Bennett, Jr. serving in that capacity for the first 26 years and Dr. William E. Hood, Jr. for 20.

Dr. Henry G. Bennett, Jr., served as Chief of Staff from the opening of the hospital in 1959 until his death in 1984.

1959
Henry G. Bennett, Jr.*

1960
J. Hartwell Dunn**
H. Thompson Avey
Robert D. Anspaugh
Elmer Ridgeway, Jr.
Henry G. Bennett, Jr.*

1961
H. Thompson Avey**
Robert D. Anspaugh
Elmer Ridgeway, Jr.
John J. Donnell
Henry G. Bennett, Jr.*

1962
Robert D. Anspaugh**
Elmer Ridgeway, Jr.
John J. Donnell
E.E. Cooke
Henry G. Bennett, Jr.*

1963
Elmer Ridgeway, Jr. **
John J. Donnell
E.E. Cooke
William Paschal
Henry G. Bennett, Jr.*

1964
John J. Donnell**
E.E. Cooke
William Paschal
J.D. Shaffer
Henry G. Bennett, Jr.*

1965
E.E. Cooke**
Lynn Harrison
Hubert M. Anderson
William Reiff
Henry G. Bennett, Jr.*

1966
Lynn Harrison**
William Paschal
Hubert M. Anderson
Charles L. Freede
Henry G. Bennett, Jr.*

1967
William Paschal**
Charles L. Freede
J.D. Shaffer
Paul D. Erwin
Henry G. Bennett, Jr.*

1968
Charles L. Freede**
J.D. Shaffer
Paul D. Erwin
Charles Harvey
Henry G. Bennett, Jr.*

1969
J.D. Shaffer**
Paul D. Erwin
Charles Harvey
R.B. Price
Henry G. Bennett, Jr.*

1970
Paul D. Erwin**
Charles Harvey
R.B. Price
J.C. Monnet
Henry G. Bennett, Jr.*

1971
Charles Harvey**
R.B. Price
J.C. Monnet
William O. Coleman
Henry G. Bennet, Jr.*

1972
R.B. Price**
J.C. Monnet
William O. Coleman
William E. Hood, Jr.
Henry G. Bennett, Jr.*

1973
J.C. Monnet**
William O. Coleman
William E. Hood, Jr.
Bobby Gene Smith
Henry G. Bennett, Jr.*

1974
William O. Coleman**
William E. Hood, Jr.
Bobby Gene Smith
Henry G. Bennett, Jr.*

1975
William E. Hood, Jr.**
Bobby Gene Smith
Robert Sukman
W. David Stuart
Henry G. Bennett, Jr.*

Chief of Staff denoted by *   President denoted by **

MEDICAL STAFF OFFICERS (Cont.)

Dr. Galen P. Robbins was one of the first cardiologist to practice at Baptist Memorial Hospital.

1976
Bobby Gene Smith**
Robert Sukman
W. David Stuart
Galen Robbins
Henry G. Bennett, Jr.*

1977
Robert Sukman**
W. David Stuart
Galen Robbins
Jerry Bressie
Henry G. Bennett, Jr.*

1978
W. David Stuart**
Galen Robbins
Jerry Bressie
Warren Felton
James B. Wise
Henry G. Bennett, Jr.*

1979
Galen Robbins**
Jerry Bressie
Warren Felton
James B. Wise
Henry G. Bennett, Jr.*

1980
Jerry Bressie**
Warren Felton
James B. Wise
Robert C. Brown
Henry G. Bennett, Jr.*

Cardiologist Dr. Jerry Bressie became an officer of the Medical Staff in 1977 and served as President in 1980.

1981
Warren Felton**
James B. Wise
Robert C. Brown
Karl K. Boatman
Henry G. Bennett, Jr.*

1982
James B. Wise**
Robert C. Brown
Karl K. Boatman
David A. Flesher
Henry G. Bennett, Jr.*

Chief of Staff denoted by *   President denoted by **

Dr. Warren Felton, a thoracic surgeon, was an original practicing doctor at Baptist Memorial Hospital and was vice president of the Medical/Dental Staff in 1979.

Dr. Merle D. Carter was an early supporter of a comprehensive Baptist Medical Center. He was president of the Medical/Dental Staff in 1989.

1983
Robert C. Brown**
Karl K. Boatman
David A. Flesher
Orville Rickey
Henry G. Bennett, Jr.*

1984
Karl K. Boatman**
David A. Flesher
Orville Rickey
Gary Roberts
Henry G. Bennett, Jr.*

1985
David A. Flesher**
Orville Rickey
Gary Roberts
William Cleaver
H.Thompson Avey*

1986
Orville Rickey**
Gary Roberts
William Cleaver
Merle Carter
H.Thompson Avey*

1987
Gary Roberts**
William Cleaver
Merle Carter
Ronald White
H.Thompson Avey*

1988
William Cleaver**
Merle Carter
Ronald White
Tommy Hewett
William E. Hood, Jr.*

Dr. David A. Flesher was an active member of the Medical Staff leadership in the early 1980s.

1989
Merle Carter**
Ronald White
Tommy Hewett
Nathan Bradley
William E. Hood, Jr.*

1990
Ronald White**
Tommy Hewett
Nathan Bradley
Dodge Hill
William E. Hood, Jr.*

1991
Tommy Hewett**
Nathan Bradley
Dodge Hill
Fenton Sanger
William E. Hood, Jr.*

MEDICAL STAFF OFFICERS (Cont.)

Dr. Orville Rickey was President of the Medical/Dental Staff in 1986.

1992
Nathan Bradley**
Dodge Hill
Fenton Sanger
Sherman Lawton
William E. Hood, Jr.*

1993
Dodge Hill**
Fenton Sanger
Sherman Lawton
William E. Hood, Jr.*
Charles F. Bethea

1994
Fenton Sanger**
Sherman Lawton
Charles F. Bethea
Paul Kanaly
William E. Hood, Jr.*

1995
Sherman Lawton**
Charles Bethea
Paul Kanaly
Aline Brown
William E. Hood, Jr.*

1996
Charles Bethea**
Paul Kanaly
Aline Brown
Don Murray
William E. Hood, Jr.*

1997
Paul Kanaly**
Aline Brown
Don Murray
John Huff
William E. Hood, Jr.*

1998
Aline Brown**
Don Murray
John Huff
Mike Seikel
William E. Hood, Jr.*

1999
Don Murray**
John Huff
Mike Seikel
V. Ramgopal
William E. Hood, Jr.*

2000
John Huff**
Mike Seikel
Vadakepat Ramgopal
Thomas Flesher, III
William E. Hood, Jr.*

2001
Mike Seikel**
Vadakepat Ramgopal
Thomas Flesher, III
Georgianne Snowden
William E. Hood, Jr.*

2002
Vadakepat Ramgopal**
Thomas Flesher, III
Georgianne Snowden
Matthew Britt
William E. Hood, Jr.*

Chief of Staff denoted by *   President denoted by **

2003
Thomas Flesher, III **
Georgianne Snowden
Matthew Britt
Dennis Parker
William E. Hood, Jr. *

2004
Georgianne Snowden **
Matthew Britt
Dennis Parker
D. Reed McNeely
William E. Hood, Jr. *

2005
Matthew Britt **
Dennis Parker
D. Reed McNeely
Sudhir Khanna
William E. Hood, Jr. *

2006
Dennis Parker **
D. Reed McNeely
Sudhir Khanna
Robert Beckerley
Matthew Britt
William E. Hood, Jr. *

2007
D. Reed McNeely **
Sudhir Khanna
Robert Beckerley
Jay Cannon
Dennis Parker
William E. Hood, Jr. *

2008
Sudhir Khanna **
Robert Beckerley
Azhar U. Khan
David S. Boggs
D. Reed McNeely
Jay Paul Cannon *

2009
Robert Beckerley**
Azhar Khan
David S. Boggs
Steve Reiter
Sudhir Khanna
Jay Paul Cannon*

2010
Azhar Khan**
David S. Boggs
Steve Reiter
Chris Davis
Robert Beckerley
Jay Paul Cannon*

2011
David S. Boggs**
Steve Reiter
Chris Davis
David S. Stokesberry
Azhar Khan
Jay Paul Cannon*

2012
Steve Reiter**
Chris Davis
David Stokesberry
Michael Kutner
David Boggs
Jay Paul Cannon*

2013
David Stokesberry**
Michael Kutner
William Cook
Richard Heigle
Steve Reiter
Jay Paul Cannon*

2014
Michael Kutner**
William Cook
Richard Heigle
Stephen Lee
David Stokesberry
Sudhir Khanna*

2015
William Cook**
Richard Heigle
Stephen Lee
Charles Elkins
Michael Kutner
Sudhir Khanna*

2016
Richard Heigle*
Stephen Lee
Charles Elkins
Vivek Kohli
William Cook
Sudhir Khanna*

VOLUNTEER AUXILIARY PRESIDENTS

Ora Mashburn	1960-1961
Helen Masheter	1962
Elizabeth Bell	1963
Dorothy Creek	1964
Verna Patteson	1965
Dorothy Hayes	1966
Phyllis Hagan	1967
Mary Hunt	1968
Loette Buckner	1968
Alice Maxey	1969
Loette Buckner	1970
Vernoy Campbell	1971
Virgie Barrett	1972
Virginia McDonald	1973
Billie Heckel	1974-1975
Dorothy Hendrie	1976
Eunice Holt	1977
Helen Musgrave	1978
Deloris Brinkley	1979
Milly Stone	1980
Emma K. McCullough	1981
Adeis Sutton	1982
Jeanne Seehorn	1983
Leah Funk	1984
Ruth Cockes	1985
Anita Bruce	1986

Alena Ingram	1987
Sharon Huffman	1988
Myrtle Seright	1989
Janice Doughty	1990
Ursula Lewis	1991
Hazel Kendrick	1992
Wanda Sellers	1993
Jean Lynch	1994
Loyce Willett	1995
Elizabeth Owen	1996
Gene Seagrove	1997
Esther Fowble	1998
Dee Shaver	1999
Karen Cox	2000
Helen Brandt	2001
Carol Koop	2002
Robert Bright	2003
Sandra Hastings	2004
Ed Noble	2005
Bill T. Schrieber	2006
Nancy Logston	2007-2008
Patsey Smith	2009
Edwin Koop	2010
Betty Hudson	2011-2012
Barbara Trumbly	2013
Sharon Williams	2014-2015
Vanessa Hunholz	2015-2016

INTEGRIS HEALTH
BOARD OF DIRECTORS, 2016

David Thompson, chairman
Peter B. Delaney, vice chairman
Christopher C. Turner, secretary and treasurer
C. Bruce Lawrence, president and CEO
Luke R. Corbett
Neal Hogan, PhD
Edmund O. Martin
Philip A. Mosca, MD
Joey Sager
Elliott R. Schwartz, DO
Marshall Snipes
Georgianne Snowden, MD
Mark Werner, MD

Courtesy Axiz Photography and Toby Nabors

EPILOGUE

I hope you enjoyed reading about the impressive history of INTEGRIS Baptist Medical Center. The religious and community leaders, physicians, clinical professionals, and administrators from the 1940s and 1950s certainly accomplished their original goal of bringing the highest possible quality care to the people of Oklahoma.

As you have read, if a medical procedure or service did not exist or was not possible in Oklahoma it was Baptist Medical Center that stepped up to bring the capability closer to home for all Oklahomans—building a comprehensive burn center, multi-organ transplant institute, advanced cancer treatment (including proton therapy), a statewide telemedicine network, advanced heart care, and countless other needed specialties to our state.

It is a history to be celebrated. However, more exciting to me is the future of Oklahoma City's INTEGRIS Baptist Medical Center. I see firsthand the world-class physicians and clinicians focused daily on improving the health of the people and communities we serve. There are no excuses and no expenses spared when it comes to ensuring that we bring to Oklahoma high-quality health care, the latest technologies and treatments, all made available to anyone who comes to our facilities. From INTEGRIS Jim Thorpe Rehabilitation's Loco-Mat and Ekso-Bionic Suit to INTEGRIS Heart Hospital's advanced arterial treatments to heart-pump assist device implants, INTEGRIS remains a leading-edge pioneer in health care.

U. S. News & World Report, for several years in a row now, ranks INTEGRIS Baptist as the #1 hospital in metro Oklahoma City as well as #1 in the State of Oklahoma. Healthgrades, Becker's Review, Oklahoma Quality Award, and Women's Choice—among many others—also rank it, year after year, as a top health care provider in the region and country.

Many INTEGRIS employees, joined by members of the television and news media, were on-hand for the official public announcement of INTEGRIS and Mayo Clinic, Excellence Working Together.

As INTEGRIS' current President and CEO, my commitment to you is a continued journey to achieve excellence, a continued focus on recruiting the finest physicians, clinicians, and visionary administrators who will all work together to place Oklahomans— and Oklahoma—at the top for access to high-quality care and advanced treatments. In January 2016, it

From left, C. Bruce Lawrence, INTEGRIS President and CEO; Jeff Bolton, Mayo Clinic Chief Administrative Officer; Dr. David Hayes, Medical Director – Mayo Clinic Care Network; David Thompson, Chairman – INTEGRIS Health Board; and Dr. James White, Medical Director, INTEGRIS, on-stage following the public announcement of the INTEGRIS, and Mayo Clinic collaboration announcement.

was my pleasure to announce INTEGRIS' selection as a member of the Mayo Clinic Care Network, a distinction enjoyed by only the highest-quality hospitals and health care organizations. The collaboration allows INTEGRIS physicians to work directly with Mayo Clinic physicians on complex diagnosis and treatment plans to complement the innovative and leading care patients have grown to expect from INTEGRIS. Our network of 19 health care campuses and more than 160 clinics across Oklahoma is testament to the vision of our early founders.

I know those founders, and early medical providers, would be pleased by what has been—and continues to be—accomplished by our INTEGRIS family today. Six out of every ten Oklahomans live within 30 miles of an INTEGRIS facility or provider. And, that early goal of "excellence on the hill" continues stronger than ever across Oklahoma today.

C. Bruce Lawrence
President and CEO

INDEX